STUDENT MATHEMATICAL LIBRA
Volume 18

Cryptography:
An Introduction

V. V. Yaschenko
Editor

AMERICAN MATHEMATICAL SOCIETY

Под редакцией В. В. Ященко

ВВЕДЕНИЕ В КРИПТОГРАФИЮ

МЦНМО–ЧеРо, Москва 1998, 2000

Translated from the Russian by Sergei Lando

2000 *Mathematics Subject Classification*. Primary 94-01, 94A60;
Secondary 11T71, 68P25.

Library of Congress Cataloging-in-Publication Data

Vvedenie v kriptografiiu. English.
    Cryptography : an introduction / V. V. Yaschenko, editor.
        p. cm. — (Student mathematical library, ISSN 1520-9121 ; v. 18)
    Includes bibliographical references.
    ISBN 0-8218-2986-6 (acid-free paper)
    1. Computer security. 2. Cryptography. I. IAshchenko, V. V. II. Title.
III. Series.

QA76.9.A25 V85   2002
005.8′2—dc21   2002027740

Contents

Contents

Preface

Cryptography, the study of ciphers, for a long time was a secret science because it was used primarily to ensure security of state and military secrets. Presently, cryptographic methods and tools are used not only by the state, but also in the private or corporate life, and classified information is not necessarily the main object of protection. The amount of information presented in the digital form and spread all over the world is now very large, and this information requires protection against nonfriendly intrusion, collection, substitution, falsification, and so on. Cryptography provides the most efficient tools for defending against these threats.

Nowadays cryptographic algorithms still remain secret for ordinary users, although many people have already applied some cryptographic means like encrypting electronic mail or smart bank cards, and so on. Naturally, the main question the user asks is whether a given cryptographic tool provides sufficient defense. However, even a precise formulation of this question is not easy. Whom are we protecting from? What are the capabilities of our opponents? What goals do they pursue? How to measure the level of security? The list of these questions can be extended. Answers to them require a knowledge of the very basics of cryptography.

The goal of this book is to give a popular explanation of these basics (we touch only upon the "nonstate" part of the science; the state security aspects must remain secret). It can also be used as a textbook.

The presentation in the book is geared towards a mathematically minded reader. The chapters are more or less independent (which sometimes requires repetition of material), and they can be read in an arbitrary order. We recommend that everybody read the introductory Chapter 1, since it describes, in a popular form, all main notions of the modern cryptography: a cipher, a key, security, an electronic digital signature, a cryptographic protocol, and so on. In other chapters the explanations are partially repeated, but on a more profound level. Some notions of university mathematics (known to university students and those high school students who take advanced mathematics classes) are used in Chapters 2, 3, 4, and 5. Chapter 6 contains problems offered at Cryptography Olympiads, and its reading does not require any knowledge beyond high school mathematics.

Warning: the cryptographic tools and software mentioned in the book only illustrate general ideas; we did not intend to evaluate or to compare the cryptographic tools available on the market.

The scientific base of cryptography owns a great deal to the outstanding American scientist Claude Shannon. The secret version of his report *"The mathematical theory of cryptography"* was prepared in 1945, made public in 1948, and translated into Russian in 1963. We recommend that everybody interested in cryptography read this paper.

A professional understanding of cryptographic algorithms and analysis of their advantages and weak points requires a serious mathematical training. The reason is that the modern cryptography is based on results from various areas, such as computational complexity, number theory, algebra, information theory, and so on. We refer the reader seriously interested in cryptography to the book *"Cryptography in banking"*, MIFI, Moscow, 1997, by M. I. Anokhin, N. P. Varnovskii, V. M. Sidelnikov, and V. V. Yaschenko (in Russian).

Chapter 1 of the present book was written by V. Yaschenko (who also served as the editor for the entire book), Chapters 2 and 3, by

N. Varnovskii, Chapter 4, by Yu. Nesterenko, Chapter 5, by G. Kabatyansky, and Chapter 6, by P. Gyrdymov, A. Zubov, A. Zyazin, and V. Ovchinnikov.

September 1998   *V. Yaschenko*

Chapter 1

Main Notions

1. Introduction

How can one transmit information without privacy violation? For sure, each reader tried to solve this problem, at one time or another, pursuing various goals and under various circumstances. (For convenience of further references we call this problem the "ST problem", that is, the *Secure Transmission* problem.) The odds are that the solution found by the reader repeated one of the ways of secure information transmission already discovered by the humankind.

It is not difficult to conclude that there are three approaches to solving the problem:

1. Establish an absolutely secure communication line between the users.

2. Use a public communication link, but hide the very fact that information was transmitted.

3. Use a public communication link, but transform the information to be transmitted in such a way that only the authorized receiver would be able to reconstruct it.

Let us make some comments concerning these possibilities.

1. Taking into account the modern state of sciences and technology it is practically impossible to construct such a secure communication line convenient for multiple transmission of large amounts of information.

2. Methods of hiding the fact that information was transmitted constitute the subject of *steganography*.

The first usage of steganography dates back to antiquity. For example, one of the known methods consisted in shaving slave's scull and writing a message on the skin. After the hair grew back, the sender sent the slave to the receiver.

Detective novels often describe various ways of writing secret messages between the lines of a plain, nonsecret text. These messages can be written either by milk, or by more complex chemicals that require further processing. One more way is to use "microdots": with modern technology, the message can be saved on a very small piece of storage medium, which is delivered together with a usual letter, say, under the stamp, or in another previously arranged place.

The wide proliferation of computers during the last decades germinated a lot of sophisticated devices for "hiding" secret information in the midst of huge information massives inside computers. An instructive example of such hiding (a text file inserted in a graphical file) can be found on the World Wide Web.[1] (For comments on this example see "Computerra", no. 48 (225), December 1 (1997), p. 62. However the authors of the paper view steganography as a part of cryptography. Of course, one may use steganography to hide encrypted texts, but, generally speaking, these two approaches to information security are essentially different.)

3. *Cryptography* studies methods of information transformation (*encryption*) providing us with information security. These methods are called *ciphers*.

Ciphering (or *encryption*) is the process of applying the cipher to the original information (the *plaintext*) according to the rules of the cipher; as the result, we obtain the *encrypted text* (or the *ciphertext*, or the *cryptogram*).

---

[1]http://www.geocities.com/SiliconValley/Vista/6001

The *decryption* process is the inverse procedure, i.e., the transformation of the cryptogram into the plaintext according to some specific rules, which are also a part of the cipher.

Cryptography is an applied science, and it is based on the most recent developments of other sciences, first of all mathematics. On the other hand, all applications and daily needs of cryptography depend on the development of technology, namely on the communication and information transmission hardware.

2. The subject of cryptography

Now, *what is the subject of cryptography?* In order to answer this question let us return to the ST problem and make both the situation and the notions more precise.

Note first of all that the problem arises only for information which must be kept private. Such information is also called *secret*, or *confidential*. The most typical and frequently occurring forms of confidential information are

- state secrets;
- military secrets;
- business and commercial secrets;
- judicial secrets;
- medical secrets, and so on.

Below, speaking about secret information, we mean the following properties of it:

- there is a group of *authorized users* of this information;
- there are *unauthorized users* intending to get the information in order to profit from it, and to harm the authorized users.

For simplicity, we start with a single threat, that of information divulgence. There are also other threats, such as information substitution or imitation; we shall discuss them later.

Now we are able to represent the ST problem in the schematic form shown in Figure 1. Here A and B are authorized users of the information who want to communicate through a public line, and O

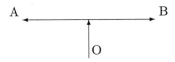

is an unauthorized user (an *adversary*, an *enemy*, or an *opponent*), who can intercept the messages and try to extract useful information from them. This formal scheme is a typical model of a situation where cryptographic information security methods are used.

Note that cryptography preserves some military terms (like an enemy, or attacking a cipher, and so on) that reflect the exact meaning of the notions. However, the well-known military terminology based on the notion of a code (naval codes, Joint Staff codes, code books, and so on) is not used in the theoretical cryptography anymore. The reason is that during the last decades *coding theory* became a huge separate science whose subject is the information transmission via communication lines with random errors. The terms "encoding" and "enciphering", previously used as synonyms, now are related to two different notions. For example, the statement "encoding is a kind of enciphering" is now incorrect.

Cryptography studies those methods of information transformation that prevent an opponent from extracting information contained in the messages he intercepted. In this approach the message communicated through the line is not the original message, but the result of its transformation using a cipher. The opponent must break the cipher, which may prove to be a complicated problem.

Cracking of a cipher is the process of extracting relevant information from an encrypted text without knowing the cipher.

However, besides intercepting and breaking a cipher the opponent may try to obtain desired information in a number of other ways. The best known of these ways consists in recruiting an agent who is one of the authorized users of the desired information, and in getting access to the information through the agent. Cryptography is powerless against such an attack.

Another threat is that the adversary, trying to get the information, may also try to destroy or to modify it during a communication session. This threat is very different from intercepting or breaking the cipher. It requires specific security methods.

Therefore, on the way from one authorized user to another, information must be protected using different tools against different threats. These tools form an information protecting chain, consisting of links of different kind, and the adversary, of course, will search for the weakest link in this chain in order to obtain the desired information at the least possible cost. This means that when developing a security strategy, the authorized users must also take into account that it makes no sense to establish a strong link if there are much weaker ones (the "equistrong link principle").

We should not forget about another important problem, namely the relation between the cost of information, of its protection, and of its extraction. Presently, the use of communication devices, as well as pick-up technology and protection devices require significant expenses. It seems reasonable, before protecting information, to ask oneself

1) whether the information is more valuable for the adversary than the cost of the attack;

2) whether the information is more valuable for me than the protection expenses.

These questions are crucial in the choice of appropriate security tools, either physical, or steganographic, or cryptographic, and so on.

Sometimes it is convenient to illustrate cryptography notions with historical examples, and we allow ourselves a brief deviation.

For a long time eccentrics were involved in cryptography. Some of them were talented scientists, diplomats, priests. During certain historic periods cryptography was even regarded as a kind of black magic. This lasted until the beginning of the 20th century, when the first encryption machines were invented. The mathematical nature of cryptography problems was understood only in the middle of the

20th century, after the seminal works of the outstanding American researcher C. Shannon.

The history of cryptography abounds with diplomacy and military secrets, and it is covered by the mist of legends. The most complete reference on the history of cryptography[2] contains more than thousand pages. A monograph devoted to the history of ciphers in Russia was published in 1994.[3]

Many historical characters were involved in cryptographic activities. Here are only a few most apparent examples. The first information about using ciphers in the war is related to the Sparta general Lysander (the cipher "Scytale"). Caesar used a cipher now known as "Caesar's cipher". The cipher later known as Politius's square was invented in ancient Greece. One of the first books devoted to cryptography was written by the abbot J. Trithemius (1462–1561) who lived in Germany. In 1566 the well-known mathematician G. Cardano published a paper about the ciphering system he invented ("Cardano's grill"). In the 16th century France enriched the culture with King's Henry IV and Richelieu's ciphers. A number of ciphers used in Russia, the "cipher alphabet" invented by Peter the Great in 1700 among them, are described in the book by Soboleva mentioned above.

Some properties of ciphers and their applications are described in fiction books, first of all in adventure, criminal and military novels. The reader can find a good detailed description of one of the simplest types of ciphers, the *substitution cipher*, and the ways of breaking it in the two well-known novels, "The golden beetle" by E. A. Poe, and "Dancing men" by A. Conan Doyl.

Consider two examples in more detail.

The "Scytale" cipher is known since the war between Sparta and Athens in the 5th century B.C. A narrow papyrus band was winded around a rod (a "scytale") without gaps and overlapping, and then the plaintext was written along the scytale's axis. After the band was unwound, a stranger could only see a meaningless sequence of

---

[2]David Kahn, *Codebreakers. The story of secret writing*, Macmillan, New York, 1967.

[3]T. A. Soboleva, *Cryptography throughout Russian history (The history of cryptography in Russia from the 18th till the beginning of the 20th century)*, Moscow, 1994.

letters. Then the band was sent to the addressee. The addressee took a similar scytale, winded the band on it in the same way, and read the message along the axis.

Note that in this cipher the transformation of a plaintext consists in permuting the letters. Therefore, the Scytale cipher belongs to the class of *permutation ciphers*.

In Caesar's cipher each letter of a plaintext is replaced with the third subsequent letter in the alphabet (the alphabet is thought of as written along a circle, and "a" follows "z"). Note that Caesar used the third letter, while other possibilities also are available. The only thing needed is that the addressee of the ciphered message also must know the shift value. The class of ciphers containing Caesar's cipher consists of *substitution ciphers*.

The discussion above shows that it is not an easy task to invent a good cipher. Therefore, it seems reasonable to increase the "life time" of a cipher so that one could encrypt as many messages as possible. However, the threat that the adversary has already broken the cipher and can read the protected information increases. If there is a replaceable key in a cipher, then changing the key we can make adversary's achievements useless.

In cryptography, a *key* is a changeable element of a cipher that can be applied for encrypting a given message. For example, the key in the Scytale cipher is the diameter of the scytale, while the key in ciphers of Caesar's type is the alphabet shift of the ciphertext with respect to the plaintext.

The argument above explains why the key constitutes the main part of information security. The cipher itself, the cipher machine, or the principle of ciphering are assumed to be known to the adversary from the very beginning, while the key, which essentially determines the transformation, remains secret. Now authorized users must securely exchange the keys, or implement the same key at opposite ends of a communication line before exchanging encrypted messages. On the other hand, the adversary faces a new task, the one of finding the key; after solving this task the adversary can easily read messages encrypted using this key.

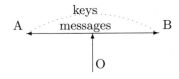

Figure 2

Return to the formal description of the central cryptography object (Figure 1). Now we must add an essential feature: a secret communication channel for exchanging keys (see Figure 2). The creation of such a channel usually is not a serious problem since it is not overloaded.

We should note now that there is no cipher that would meet all requirements. The choice of the encryption procedure depends on the nature of the information, its value, and the abilities of the information owners. Let us underline first of all the variety of forms of information to be protected: there is paper, telephone, visual, computer, and so on information. Each kind of information has its own specific features, and these features have serious influence on the choice of encryption methods. The amount and the required speed of information transmission also play a crucial role. The type of the cipher and its parameters depend essentially on the nature of the secrets to be protected. Some secrets (say, state, military, and so on) must remain covered for decades, while others (stock information, for example) may be made public in a few hours. The personality of the adversary also must be taken into account. There is a big difference between an individual or even a gang of criminals on one side and a powerful state institution on the other side.

The ability of a cipher to resist various attacks is called "cipher's security". An "attack on a cipher" is an attempt to break the cipher.

The notion of cipher's security is one of the central notions in cryptography. Although its meaning is clear from the qualitative point of view, no strict estimates of the security for a given cipher are known. The reason is that there is a lack of required mathematical statements (we are going to discuss this problem below). This is why the only way to estimate cipher's security is to try to break it; the estimates thus obtained depend, therefore, on the qualifications of the *cryptanalysts* who attack the cipher. Sometimes this procedure is called *security testing*.

The important preliminary stage in security testing is the analysis of possible ways of adversary's attacks on the cipher. Usually these ways are not related to cryptography. Hence, the available estimates of ciphers' security always contain the list of assumptions about the adversary's goals and abilities.

First of all, as was already mentioned, we usually assume that the adversary knows the cipher and has an opportunity to analyze it in advance. The adversary also is aware of some parameters of the plaintexts, like the main subject, style, some standards, formats, and so on.

Here are other examples of more specific abilities of the adversary:

– the adversary can pick up all ciphered messages, while he has no access to the corresponding plaintexts;

– the adversary can pick up all ciphered messages, and he also has access to all corresponding plaintexts;

– the adversary has an access to the cipher (but not to the keys!), and therefore he is able to encrypt and decrypt arbitrary information.

In conclusion, let us make a terminology remark. The term "cryptology" is used nowadays as frequently as the word "cryptography", but the relationship between the two is usually not well understood. The formation of these areas of science is now completed, and the subject and the methodology of each of them becomes more precise.

Cryptography is the field of engineering concerned with mathematical techniques in information security; consists of cryptosynthesis and cryptanalysis.

Cryptosynthesis is the part of cryptography concerned with developing cryptographic aids for information security.

Cryptanalysis is a collection of aids and methods for cracking cryptographic schemes.

Theoretical (mathematical) cryptography is the field of computer science studying mathematical models of cryptographic schemes.

The relationship between cryptography and cryptanalysis is obvious: cryptography is a defense, while cryptanalysis is an attack on ciphers. However, these two areas are closely related, and each good cryptographer is also a cryptanalyst.

3. Mathematical basis

The development of cryptography was seriously influenced by the work of the American mathematician Claude Shannon. His papers formed a foundation of information theory; he also developed the required mathematical background for research in many areas related to information. Moreover, the date of publication of Shannon's paper "*A mathematical theory of communication*"[4] is the birthday of information theory.

In his paper "*Communication theory of secrecy systems*"[5] Shannon gathered the experience existed in cipher development. It turned out that even most complicated ciphers contain, as building blocks, simple ciphers such as *substitution ciphers*, *permutation ciphers*, or their mixtures.

Substitution ciphers are the simplest and most popular ones. Typical examples are Caesar's cipher, Peter the Great's "cipher alphabet", and the "dancing men" invented by Conan Doyl. We see from the name that a substitution cipher transforms letters or other parts of a plaintext into letters or other parts of the cryptogram. A mathematical description of a substitution cipher is very easy. Let X, Y be two alphabets (the plaintext is written in X, while the cryptogram is written in Y) containing the same number of letters, and let $g : X \to Y$ be a one-to-one mapping. The corresponding substitution cipher transforms a plaintext $x_1 x_2 \ldots x_n$ to the cryptogram $g(x_1)g(x_2)\ldots g(x_n)$.

A permutation cipher, as we can see from the name, permutes letters in a plaintext. A typical example of a permutation cipher

---

[4]Bell System Techn. J., vol. 27 (1948), 379–423; 623–656.
[5]Bell System Techn. J., vol. 28 (1949), 656–715.

is the Scytale cipher. Usually, a plaintext is divided into blocks of equal length, and each block is encrypted independently. Suppose, for example, the length of each block is n, and σ is a one-to-one mapping of the set $\{1, 2, \ldots, n\}$ into itself. The corresponding permutation cipher looks as follows: a block $x_1 \ldots x_n$ of a plaintext is transformed into the block $x_{\sigma(1)} \ldots x_{\sigma(n)}$ of the cryptogram.

The crucial point for the development of cryptography is Shannon's theorem on the existence and uniqueness of a perfectly secure cipher. Any such cipher is a version of the so-called "one-way tape", which "concatenates" plaintexts with a random key of the same length.

The proof of this result is based on an information-theoretical method of studying ciphers developed by Shannon. We are not going to discuss it here in detail, and refer the reader to Shannon's paper.

Let us describe main features of the secure cipher and possibilities of its practical use. A typical, and the simplest, example of implementation of the perfectly secure cipher is the Vernam cipher. This cipher produces the bit sum of an n-bit plaintext and an n-bit key:

$$y_i = x_i \oplus k_i, \quad i = 1, \ldots, n.$$

Here $x_1 \ldots x_n$ is a plaintext, $k_1 \ldots k_n$ is the key, and $y_1 \ldots y_n$ is the cryptogram.

Let us emphasize that each of the following requirements is crucial for the perfect security of the one-way tape:

1) the keys must be absolutely random (all keys have the same probability); this means, in particular, that we cannot produce a key by a deterministic device;

2) the length of the key must coincide with that of the plaintext;

3) each key can be used only once.

If at least one of these requirements is violated, then the cipher stops being perfectly secure, and there are theoretical possibilities to break it (although these possibilities can be hard to realize).

However, it turns out that exactly these requirements make the perfectly secure cipher too expensive and inefficient. Before using it we must supply each user with a sufficient set of random keys avoiding the occurrence of coinciding keys, and this is difficult and expensive.

For all these reasons, perfectly secure ciphers are used only in networks with small amount of information transmitted (usually these are very important state networks).

In practice, authorized owners of information are forced to use ciphers that are not perfectly secure. These ciphers can be broken, at least in principle. The main problem is whether the adversary will have enough time and resources for developing required algorithms. It is clear that an adversary with unbounded resources can break any cipher that is not perfectly secure.

What is the right behavior for a legal user when choosing a cipher? The best way would be to prove that no adversary will manage to break the cipher, say, for 10 years, and to obtain in this way a theoretical security bound. Unfortunately, the available mathematical theory does not provide required theorems. The *problem of lower bounds for computational complexity* remains an unsolved problem.

Therefore, in practice one must use an alternative approach, namely, derive so-called practical estimates for security. To this end we have to do the following:

– first, we must specify our adversary precisely; we must be aware of what the adversary knows or can learn about the encrypting system, as well as what are the resources he can put together to break the cipher;

– we must put ourselves in adversary's place and try to attack the encryption system from his position, i.e., to develop various algorithms for breaking the cipher; we must do our best to model the resources available for the adversary;

– the best algorithm must be used to obtain a practical estimate of the cipher security.

It is useful to illustrate this layout with the following two ways of breaking a cipher: a random choice of the key (which works with small probability, but the complexity of the method is also small), and the exhaustive search through all possible keys until the required key will be found (this method works in an arbitrary situation, but its complexity is extremely high). Note also that we do not always need to attack the key: some ciphers allow one to reconstruct the plaintext from an encrypted one without knowing the key.

4. New directions

It is said in the book "*Codes and mathematics*" by A. N. Arshinov and L. E. Sadovskii published in 1983 that "There are many ways of secret writing, and there is no need to invent new ways." This was, however, yet another great misconception concerning cryptography. The authors were not aware of the paper "*New directions in cryptography*" by W. Diffie and M. Hellman[6] which led not only to a modification of cryptography, but also to the birth and fast development of new directions in mathematics itself. The main notion of the "new cryptography" is that of a one-way function (see a more detailed discussion in Chapter 2).

A mapping $F : X \to Y$ is a *one-way function* if it possesses the following two properties:

a) there is a polynomial algorithm for computing $F(x)$ given x;

b) there are no polynomial algorithms for *inverting* the function F, i.e., for solving the equation $F(x) = y$ with respect to x for a given y (see the precise definition in Chapter 2).

Note that a one-way function differs essentially from the functions we are familiar with from calculus courses because of the restrictions on the computational complexity of the function and its inverse. The problem of the existence of one-way functions remains open.

Another new notion is that of a *function with a secret*. The name *trapdoor function* is also commonly used. A *trapdoor function* is a mapping $F : K \times X \to Y$ such that

a) there exists a polynomial time algorithm that picks a pair (k_1, k_2) such that k_1 is a random element of the set K. The value k_2 is called the trapdoor;

b) there exists a polynomial time algorithm that computes $f(k_1, x)$ for given k_1 and $x \in X$;

---

[6]IEEE Trans. Inform. Theory **IT-22** (1976), no. 6, 644–654.

c) no polynomial time algorithm that knows k_1 but not k_2 can invert the function $F(k_1, \cdot)$;

d) there exists a polynomial time algorithm inverting the function $F(k_1, \cdot)$ when the trapdoor k_2 is known.

The existence of a function with a secret also remains an open problem. A number of functions that presumably are trapdoor functions were constructed for practical cryptography usage. No proofs of condition c) for these functions are known, but it is either proved or assumed that the problem of inverting such a function is computationally equivalent to a well-studied intractable mathematical problem. The best known and most popular of them is the number-theoretic function on which the RSA algorithm is based.

Using functions with secrets in cryptography allows one to

1) establish an exchange of encrypted messages through open communication lines, i.e., to get rid of the prior secret key exchange;

2) insert a computationally hard mathematical problem in the cipher breaking problem and increase in this way the justified security level;

3) solve new cryptography problems rather than just the encryption problem (*electronic digital signature*, and so on).

Note that all these tasks can be accomplished, at least theoretically, with trapdoor functions, but solutions based on such functions are usually much simpler and more efficient.

Let us describe, for example, how to implement option 1). A user A who wishes to get cryptograms chooses a function F_K with a secret K. He makes the description of the function F_K (the encryption algorithm) available to all potential participants (by publishing the algorithm, for example), but keeps K secret. Now, if a user B wants to send protected information $x \in X$ to A, then he computes $y = F_K(x)$ and sends y to A through a public communication line. Since A knows how to invert F_K for his own key K, he can reconstruct x from the received cryptogram y. Since nobody else knows K, nobody can, by property b) of trapdoor functions, reconstruct the protected information x from the encrypted message $F_K(x)$ in polynomial time.

The system described above is called a *cryptosystem with public key* since the encryption algorithm F_K is public. Such systems also acquire the name *asymmetric*: the encryption and decryption algorithms in them are distinct. On the contrary, traditional ciphers are called *symmetric*: the encrypting and the decrypting keys for them coincide. The encryption algorithm for asymmetric systems is public, but the decryption algorithm cannot be recovered in polynomial time.

Diffie and Hellman also suggested to apply the above idea to the implementation of an electronic (digital) signature that cannot be falsified in polynomial time. Suppose a user A wants to sign a message x. Knowing the secret K he finds y such that $F_K(y) = x$ and sends to a user B the message x together with the digital signature y. The user B keeps the signature y, which proves that A has signed the message x.

A message signed electronically is a pair (x, y), where x is the message, and y is the solution of the equation $F_K(y) = x$; here $F_K : X \to Y$ is a function with a secret that is known to all interacting users. The properties of the function F_K obviously imply the following useful properties of the digital signature:

1) only the user possessing the given secret K can sign a message x, i.e., solve the equation $F_K(y) = x$; in other words, there is no way to falsify the signature;

2) any user who knows the public key, that is, the function F_K, can verify the legitimacy of the signature;

3) there is no way to reject the legitimacy of a signature in the case of a conflict;

4) signed messages (x, y) can be sent through any communication lines without any threat of security violation.

In addition to the principle of constructing cryptosystems with public keys, Diffie and Hellmann suggested another new idea, the *public key distribution*, in the same paper. They asked the following question: is there a way to organize interaction between two users A and B through public communication lines solving the following problem:

1) before an interaction session starts, A and B share no secret information, but such information is a result of the session, i.e., the session produces the information;

2) no passive adversary that picks up all messages and knows the goals of A and B can reconstruct the common secret key generated by A and B.

Diffie and Hellmann suggested a way to solve these problems using the function

$$F(x) = \alpha^x \mod p,$$

where p is a large prime number, x is an arbitrary positive integer, and α is a *primitive element* of the finite field $\mathbb{F}_p$. The problem of inverting the function $\alpha^x \mod p$, i.e., the discrete logarithm problem, is well known to be a hard mathematical problem. (See details in Chapter 4.)

The session, or in other words, the *key generating protocol*, works as follows.

Each of the users A and B chooses independently an integer, say, x_A and x_B respectively, and keeps it secret. Then each of them computes the new integer

$$y_A = \alpha^{x_A} \mod p, \quad y_B = \alpha^{x_B} \mod p.$$

(Both numbers α and p are supposed to be public.) Then they exchange the computed numbers through a public communication line. After receiving y_B the user A computes, knowing his own secret element x_A, the new element

$$y_B^{x_A} \mod p = (\alpha^{x_B})^{x_A} \mod p,$$

and the user B does the same:

$$y_A^{x_B} = (\alpha^{x_A})^{x_B} \mod p.$$

As a result, the users A and B possess a common element $\alpha^{x_A x_B}$ of the field. This element is chosen for the common secret key of A and B.

We see from the description of the protocol that the adversary knows p, α, α^{x_A}, α^{x_B}, but not x_A and x_B, and he wants to find

$\alpha^{x_A x_B}$. No ways to do this except for discrete logarithm are known by now, and finding the latter is a computationally hard problem.

The achievements in the development of digital signature schemes and public key distribution allowed one to apply the same ideas to other problems of the interaction of remote users. This process led to the development of another direction in theoretic cryptography, cryptographic protocols (see a more detailed description in Chapter 3).

The theory of cryptographic protocols studies interaction of distant users through public communication lines. The goal of an interaction session is a fulfillment of some task. The adversary pursues his own objectives. In different problems, the adversary is supposed to possess different resources: for example, he can interact with the users under the names of other users, or intervene in information exchange processes between other users, and so on. An adversary may even turn out to be a user or a group of users.

Here are a few more examples of tasks arising in distant interaction (we advise the reader to invent his own tasks).

1. Two users distrusting each other want to sign an agreement. The signing procedure must prevent the situation where one of the users receives a copy of the agreement signed by the other one, but without his own signature.

A protocol performing this task is called an *agreement signature protocol*.

2. Two users distrusting each other want to flip the coin. This should be done in a way that prevents the user flipping the coin from changing the result after receiving the guess from the other user.

A protocol performing this task is a *coin flipping protocol*.

Let us describe one of the simplest coin flipping protocols (the so-called Blum–Micali scheme). It can be realized if both users A and B have a one-way function $f : X \to Y$ meeting the following conditions:

1) X is a set of integers containing the same number of odd and even integers;

2) any two elements $x_1, x_2 \in X$ with coinciding image $f(x_1) = f(x_2)$ have the same parity;

3) it is "difficult" to compute the parity of an unknown value x from its image $f(x)$.

The role of the coin flipping is played by a uniform random choice of an element $x \in X$, and the parity of x plays the role of heads and tails. Let A be the user flipping the coin, and let B be the user who guesses. The protocol consists of the following rounds:

1) the user A chooses x ("flips the coin"), encrypts x, i.e., computes the value $y = f(x)$, and sends y to B;

2) the user B receives y, tries to guess the parity of x, and sends the guess to A;

3) after receiving the guess from B the user A informs B whether the guess is correct;

4) the user B checks that A was honest by computing $f(x)$ and comparing the result with the value y received in the second round.

3. A user A wants to prove to a user B that he is A indeed, and not an adversary (a typical example: A is a bank customer, and B is the bank).

Protocols performing this task are called *user identification protocols*.

4. A number of distant users getting orders from one center interact. Some of the users, including the center, can be adversaries. We require a common strategy allowing the users to win. This problem carries the name of the "Bysanthine generals problem", and protocols performing it are "protocols of the Bysanthine agreement".

The analysis of various protocols and ways of constructing them led to the creation in 1985–1986 of two important mathematical models: the "interactive proof" and "zero-knowledge proof" systems. The mathematical study of these new objects produced many statements useful in the development of cryptographic protocols (see Chapter 2 for a detailed discussion).

An interactive proof system (P, V, S) is a protocol for the interaction of two users: P (the prover) and V (the verifier). The user P wants to prove a statement S to the user V. It is assumed that V cannot verify the statement S without the help of P (that is why V is called the verifier). The user P can well be an adversary who wants to prove S to V, although S is false. The protocol can consist of a number of *rounds* of message exchanges between P and V, and it must satisfy the following conditions:

1) *completeness*: if S is true, then P will be able to convince the user V;

2) *correctness*: if S is false, then the probability that P will be able to convince V that S is true is small.

The last condition requires a precise mathematical formulation.

Let us emphasize that this definition does not allow V to be an adversary. And what will happen if V is an adversary and tries to "extract" some information that is new to him about the statement S? Of course, in this case the user P wants the protocol (P, V, S) to stop V from doing this. A protocol (P, V, S) performing this task is called a zero-knowledge proof, and it must satisfy, apart from conditions 1) and 2), the additional condition

3) *zero knowledge*: the user V cannot increase his knowledge about the statement S, or, in other words, he will not know why the statement S is true.

5. Conclusion

In the last few years cryptography and cryptographic protocols became a part of our everyday life. Here are a few examples. When sending an e-mail, we are sometimes asked "Do you need encoding?" An owner of a smart bank card addressing the bank through a terminal starts with the card authentication. Users of the Internet surely know about discussions concerning the adoption of the digital signature standard for pages containing crucial information (legal information, price lists, and so on). Recently network users started including not only the now familiar e-mail address, but also the less common "Public key imprint ... ".

The number of examples increases daily. These new applications of cryptography form one of the incentives for its further development.

Chapter 2

Cryptography and Complexity Theory

1. Introduction

There are two main approaches to defining the security of a cryptosystem or a cryptographic protocol (below we use the unifying term a *cryptographic scheme* for both notions) in theoretical cryptography, namely, the information theory approach and the complexity theory approach. Under the information theory approach, we assume that the adversary does not have even theoretical possibility to obtain the required information. The classical example here is the Vernam cipher with a one-time pad, which is perfectly secure against a passive adversary.

In practice, the security level of the overwhelming majority of cryptographic schemes is not that high. Moreover, it is usually easy to suggest an algorithm for the adversary to perform the information retrieval task, at least in principle. Consider the following example.

Example 1 (Public key cryptosystems). A *public key cryptosystem* is completely determined by three algorithms: the key generation algorithm, the encryption algorithm and the decryption algorithm. The key generation algorithm G is public; anybody may feed it with a random string r of required length and get a pair of keys (K_1, K_2) as the output. The open key K_1 becomes public, and the secret key K_2 and the random string r remain private. The encryption algorithm E_{K_1} and the decryption algorithm D_{K_2} are such that if (K_1, K_2) is a pair of keys generated by the algorithm G, then $D_{K_2}(E_{K_1}(m)) = m$ for an arbitrary plaintext m. We assume, for simplicity, that the ciphertext has the same length n as the plaintext. Also, we assume that the plaintext, the cryptogram, and both keys are binary strings.

Now, suppose an adversary attacks this cryptosystem. He knows the public key K_1, but not the secret key K_2. After tapping into a cryptogram d, the adversary tries to find the message m such that $d = E_{K_1}(m)$. Since the encryption algorithm is public, it is possible simply to search through all messages m_i of length n, to apply the encryption algorithm to each such message, and to compare the encrypted message $d_i = E_{K_1}(m_i)$ with d. The message m such that $d = E_{K_1}(m)$ is the required one. With a bit of luck, the answer will be found sufficiently quickly. In the worst case the search will take time proportional to $2^n T(n)$, where $T(n)$ is the time required for the computation of E_{K_1} on a message of length n. If the message length is about 1000 bits, then no computer can carry on such an exhaustive search.

This is the first way to attack a cryptosystem. This algorithm of searching for the plaintext is called the exhaustive search algorithm, or the brute force method. Another simple algorithm is the try-and-guess method. This obvious algorithm requires very short calculations, but the success probability is extremely low (if the text is sufficiently long). In practice, an adversary can attack a cryptosystem in various ways and use much more sophisticated techniques to find the plaintext. It is natural to view a cryptosystem as secure if any such algorithm requires an amount of calculations not available in practice, or if the probability of success is negligible. (We must take into account that the adversary can use randomized algorithms as well as deterministic ones.) This is the complexity theory approach to the security definition. In order to make it precise we must

1) give a formal definition of a scheme of a given type;

2) give a formal definition of the security of this scheme;

3) know how to prove that a scheme of a given type is secure.

A number of problems arises on this way.

First, in a specific cryptographic scheme the values of parameters are fixed. For example, a standard cryptosystem uses keys of length, say, 256 or 512 bits. On the contrary, the complexity analysis requires an asymptotic setting. In this approach, mathematical models of cryptographic schemes are studied. These models depend on a parameter, called the security parameter, which can take arbitrary large values (usually it runs over all natural numbers).

Second, the definition of security depends on the task the adversary tries to perform and on the information about the scheme available to him. The definition of security must be given and analyzed in each case separately.

Third, we state precisely what amount of calculations should be considered nonrealizable. The discussion above implies that this value cannot be constant; it must be a function of the growing security parameter. According to Edmond's thesis, an algorithm is considered to be efficient if the computation time is bounded by a polynomial in the input length (in the security parameter in our case). Otherwise the computations by means of the given algorithm are considered to be infeasible. Note also that the cryptographic schemes themselves *must be* efficient, i.e., all the required calculations should take at most polynomial time.

Finally, we must give a bound for the negligible probability. The standard cryptographic agreement treats the probability as negligible if it does not exceed $1/p(n)$ for an arbitrary polynomial p and for all sufficiently large values of the security parameter n.

Accepting the definitions above, we reduce the problem to proving the nonexistence of a polynomial time algorithm performing the adversary's task. However, here we encounter an extremely serious obstacle: the modern state of complexity theory does not allow one to justify superpolynomial lower bounds for problems of a given class. This means that all the known proofs of security are based on some unproved assumptions. This is why the research is usually concentrated on the search for the weakest possible sufficient (or necessary and sufficient, if available) conditions for the existence of secure schemes of each type. The assumptions are usually either general (or complexity theory based) assumptions, or number theory assumptions, that is, assumptions concerning the intractability of some number theory problems. Both these types are usually called cryptographic.

Below, we review briefly some interesting mathematical objects arising on the boundary between complexity theory and cryptography. A more detailed survey can be found in [**5**].

2. Cryptography and the $P \neq NP$ conjecture

Even mathematicians who are not specialists in complexity theory are usually familiar with the classes P and NP and the famous $P \neq NP$ conjecture.

Let us recall briefly the necessary notions. Let Σ^* denote the set of all finite sequences in the two-letter alphabet $\Sigma = \{0, 1\}$. In complexity theory, subsets $L \subseteq \Sigma^*$ are usually called *languages*. A Turing machine[1] M is called *polynomial time* if there is a polynomial p such that M stops at each input word of length n after executing at most $p(n)$ operations. A Turing machine M *recognizes* a language L if it stops in the accepting state for each input word $x \in L$, and it stops in the rejecting state for each input word $y \notin L$. The class P consists of all languages recognizable by a polynomial time Turing machine. A function $f : \Sigma^* \to \Sigma^*$ is *computable in polynomial time* if there exists a polynomial time Turing machine such that, taking a word $x \in \Sigma^*$ as an input, the word $f(x)$ is written on the tape when it stops. A language L belongs to the class NP if there is a predicate $P(x, y) : \Sigma^* \times \Sigma^* \to \{0, 1\}$ computable in polynomial time and a polynomial p such that $L = \{x | \exists y P(x, y) \& |y| \leq p(|x|)\}$. Thus, L belongs to the class NP if for any word of length n in L we can guess a string of length polynomial in n and then verify our conjecture by means of the predicate P. Obviously, $P \subseteq NP$. Whether this inclusion is strict, is one of the most famous unsolved mathematical

---

[1] For a good introduction to Turing machines, see, e.g., [**69**, Chapter 1]. (*Added in translation.*)

problems.[2] The majority of researchers think that the inclusion is indeed strict (that is, $P \neq NP$). The class NP contains a subclass of languages of maximal complexity (so-called *NP-complete* languages); an NP-complete language is polynomial only if P=NP.

Below, we shall also need the notion of a probabilistic Turing machine. The new state of an ordinary Turing machine (which is also called *deterministic*) is totally determined by the current state and the tape symbol under the head. The new state of a probabilistic machine may depend also on a random variable taking values $0, 1$ with probability $1/2$. A different approach consists in considering an additional tape containing an infinite random binary string. The random tape can be read in only one direction, and the new state of the machine can depend on the symbol under the head on the random tape.

Now let us turn to the following natural question: is the validity of the $P \neq NP$ conjecture a necessary and sufficient condition for the existence of secure cryptographic schemes?

The necessity of this condition is obvious in many cases. Let us return to Example 1 at the beginning of this chapter. Define the following language:

$$L = \{(K_1, d, i) \mid \text{there is a message } m \text{ such that } E_{K_1}(m) = d$$
$$\text{and the } i\text{th bit of } m \text{ is } 1\}.$$

It is clear that $L \in$ NP: instead of the exhaustive search described in the Introduction we can simply guess the plaintext m and verify whether $E_{K_1}(m) = d$ and the ith bit of m is 1 in polynomial time. If these statements are true, then the word (K_1, d, i) is approved; otherwise it is rejected.

If $P = NP$, then there is a deterministic algorithm recognizing the language L. Taking K_1 and d as the input this algorithm determines the plaintext m bit by bit. Therefore, this cryptosystem is insecure.

The same approach (guess the secret key and verify the correctness of the guess in polynomial time) is applicable, in principle, to

---

[2]See, for example, the URL of the Clay Mathematics Institute, http://www.claymath.org/prizeproblems/index.htm.

other cryptographic schemes as well. However, some cases cause technical difficulties related to the nonunique recovering of the required value (the plaintext, the secret key, and so on).

Turning to the sufficiency of the condition $P \neq NP$, it is natural to choose an NP-complete problem and to use it for the construction of a cryptographic scheme such that the corresponding break-in problem is NP-complete. Such attempts, related first of all to cryptographic systems with a public key, were made in the early eighties, but failed. These attempts led to the following conclusion: even if $P \neq NP$, any NP-complete problem may happen to be difficult only on a certain infinite sequence of input words. In other words, the definition of the class NP measures the complexity in the worst case, whereas the security of a cryptographic scheme requires adversary's task to be complex "almost everywhere". Hence, it became clear that the $N \neq NP$ assumption must be replaced with a much more restrictive one. For this restrictive assumption, the existence of one-way functions was chosen.

3. One-way functions

Informally speaking, a one-way function is an efficiently computable function such that there are no efficient algorithms for inverting it.[3] By inverting a function we understand a process of finding an (arbitrary) preimage of a given value in the target space (note that, generally speaking, it may happen that there is no inverse function).

Since the notion of one-way function is central in mathematical cryptography, we present a formal definition.

Let $\Sigma^n = \{0,1\}^n$ denote the set of all binary strings of length n. A function f is a family of functions $\{f_n\}$, $f_n : \Sigma^n \to \Sigma^m$, where

---

[3]There exists the following real-life analog of the notion of one-way function. Suppose we have a large telephone book where subscribers' names are listed in the alphabetical order. Then it is rather easy to find a telephone number given the name. But what about the opposite task: to find the name given a telephone number? The same example can be used to clarify the intuition behind the notion of trapdoor function (see Chapter 1). Now we have two telephone books. The first is ordered by names as above, the second, by telephone numbers. The first book is made publicly available, while we keep the second as our secret. The task to find subscriber's name given a telephone number remains intractable for anyone but us.

$m = m(n)$. For simplicity we assume that n runs over the entire set of positive integers, and that each mapping f_n is defined everywhere.

A function f is *honest* if there is a polynomial q such that $n \leq q(m(n))$ for all n.

Definition 1. An honest function f is called a *one-way function* if the following conditions are satisfied.

1) There is a polynomial algorithm producing the output $f(x)$ for each input x.

2) Let A be an arbitrary polynomial probabilistic Turing machine and x a random string from Σ^n (we use the notation $x \in_R \Sigma^n$). Then for any polynomial p and for all sufficiently large n we have

$$\Pr\{f(A(f(x))) = f(x)\} < \frac{1}{p(n)}.$$

The probability here is determined by the random choice of x and the random data used by the machine A.

Condition 2) means essentially that any polynomial time probabilistic Turing machine A can reconstruct x from a given y only with a negligibly small probability.

Note that the honesty requirement is important. If f shrinks input words too much, then A may require more than polynomial time in m, the length of $f(x)$, simply for writing out the input word.

It is clear that if a one-way function exists, then $P \neq NP$. It can happen, however, that $P \neq NP$ and there are no one-way functions.

The existence of one-way functions is necessary for the security of many types of cryptographic systems. In some cases this fact is rather simple. Let us return to Example 1. Consider a function f such that $f(r) = K_1$. The algorithm G computes it in polynomial time. Let us show that if f is not a one-way function, then the cryptosystem is insecure. Suppose there exists a polynomial time algorithm A inverting f with probability at least $1/p(n)$ for some polynomial p. Here n is the length of K_1. The adversary can use the key K_1 as the input for the algorithm A and obtain some preimage $r' \in f^{-1}(K_1)$ with probability at least $1/p(n)$. Using r' as the input for G the adversary obtains a pair of keys (K_1, K_2'). Although K_2' does not necessarily coincide with K_2, we have $D_{K_2'}(E_{K_1}(m)) = m$ for any plaintext m, by definition of a cryptosystem. Since the probability of finding K_2' is at least $1/p(n)$, and this value is not negligible, this cryptosystem is insecure.

For other cryptographic schemes, the proof is not so simple. The necessity of the existence of one-way functions for security of a number of cryptographic schemes is proved by Impagliazzo and Luby in [**38**].

It follows from the discussion above that the assumption about the existence of one-way functions is the weakest possible cryptographic assumption sufficient for the existence of secure cryptographic schemes of different types. The efforts of specialists in theoretical cryptography are concentrated on understanding whether this assumption is indeed sufficient. The following example shows that this problem is in fact complicated. Suppose f is a one-way function, and we are trying to construct a *cryptosystem with a secret key*. In such a system, there is only one key, and this key is known both to the sender of the encrypted text and to the recipient. The encryption algorithm E_K and the decryption algorithm D_K depend on this secret key K and satisfy the condition $D_K(E_K(m)) = m$ for any plaintext m. It is clear that if the adversary intercepts the ciphertext $d = f(m)$, then he can reconstruct m only with a negligible probability. But if f is a one-way function, then how can the legal recipient of d reconstruct the text m? Besides, if f is a one-way function, this only means that the adversary cannot compute the entire message. And this is a rather low security level. One would expect that an adversary knowing the cryptogram d should not be able to compute even a single bit of the plaintext.

By now, it is proved that the existence of one-way functions is a necessary and sufficient condition for the existence of secure cryptosystems with a secret key, as well as secure cryptographic protocols of various types, including electronic signature protocols. On the other hand, the result of Impagliazzo and Rydich [**40**] confirms rather strongly that the security of some types of cryptographic schemes (including key distribution protocols of Diffie–Hellman type) requires more restrictive assumptions than simply the existence of one-way functions. However, we cannot explain this result in the present chapter.

4. Pseudorandom generators

The Vernam cipher uses one-time pads. Is it possible to get rid of this defect at the expense of some weakening of the security? Here is one way to solve this problem. Suppose the sender and the recipient have a common secret key K of length n and generate a sequence $r = g(K)$ of some length $q(n)$, where q is a polynomial, by means of a sufficiently efficient algorithm g. Such a cryptosystem (we denote it by Cr) allows one to encrypt a single message or a sequence of messages m of length up to $q(n)$ bits using the formula $d = r \oplus m$, where m is the bitwise sum modulo 2. The decryption is given by the formula $m = d \oplus r$. Shannon's results imply that such a cryptosystem is not perfectly secure, that is, not secure against an arbitrary adversary (this statement is easy to verify directly). But what if we deal with a polynomially restricted adversary having only polynomial time probabilistic algorithms at his disposal? What conditions should the sequence r and the algorithm g satisfy to make the cryptosystem Cr secure? The search for an answer to this question has led to the notion of pseudorandom generator introduced by Blum and Micali in [**12**].

Let $g : \{0,1\}^n \to \{0,1\}^{q(n)}$ be a function computable in polynomial time in n. Such a function is called a *generator*. Informally, a generator g is *pseudorandom* if the sequences it generates cannot be distinguished from random sequences of the same length $q(n)$ by a polynomial time probabilistic algorithm. The formal definition is as follows.

Let A be a polynomial time probabilistic Turing machine fed with binary strings of length $q(n)$ and generating a single bit. Set

$$P_1(A, n) = \Pr\{A(r) = 1 \mid r \in_R \{0,1\}^{q(n)}\}.$$

Here the probability is the function of the random choice of the message r and random values the machine A uses. Let

$$P_2(A, n) = \Pr\{A(g(s)) = 1 \mid s \in_R \{0,1\}^n\}.$$

Here the probability is the function of the random choice of the string s and random values the machine A uses. We emphasize that the function g is computed by a deterministic algorithm.

Definition 2. A generator g is called a *cryptographically secure pseudorandom generator* if for each polynomial time probabilistic Turing machine A, every polynomial p, and all sufficiently large n we have

$$|P_1(A, n) - P_2(A, n)| < 1/p(n).$$

For brevity, cryptographically secure pseudorandom generators will be called just pseudorandom generators. This abbreviation is standard in the literature.

It is easy to show that the existence of pseudorandom generators implies the existence of one-way functions. Indeed, g itself must be a one-way function. We leave the proof of this simple fact as an exercise to the reader. The question on whether the existence of pseudorandom functions is also sufficient for the existence of pseudorandom generators remained open for a long time. In 1982, Yao [**67**] constructed a pseudorandom generator under the assumption that there are *one-way permutations*, i.e., length-preserving bijective one-way functions. In a subsequent series of papers this assumption was weakened, and finally, in 1989–1990, Impagliazzo, Levin, and Luby [**39**] and Håstad [**37**] obtained the following result.

Theorem 1. *Pseudorandom generators exist if and only if one-way functions exist.*

Pseudorandom generators are useful not only in cryptography, but also in complexity theory and in other areas of discrete mathematics. We are not going to discuss these applications in the present chapter. Instead, we illustrate their usefulness with the cryptosystem Cr described at the beginning of this section, where for the algorithm g we use a pseudorandom generator.

First of all, we must define the security of a cryptosystem with a secret key. Let E_K be the encryption algorithm of a cryptosystem with a secret key. Denote the result by $d = E_K(m)$; here K is a secret key consisting of n bits, and m is a plaintext consisting of $q(n)$ bits. Let m_i denote the ith bit of the plaintext. Let A be a polynomial time probabilistic Turing machine fed with the ciphertext d and producing the pair (i, σ), where $i \in \{1, \ldots, q(n)\}$, $\sigma \in \{0, 1\}$. Informally, a cryptosystem is secure if there is no Turing machine A that can compute some bit of the plaintext with probability essentially greater than that obtained by a simple guess.

Definition 3. A cryptosystem is *secure* if for any polynomial time probabilistic Turing machine A, any polynomial p, and all sufficiently large n we have

$$\Pr\{A(d) = (i, \sigma) \,\&\, \sigma = m_i \mid K \in_R \{0, 1\}^n, m \in_R \{0, 1\}^{q(n)}\}$$
$$< 1/2 + 1/p(n).$$

The probability (for brevity, we use the notation Pr for it below) is a function of the random choice of the secret key K, the random choice of the plaintext m in the set of all binary strings of length $q(n)$, and random variables used by the machine A.

Let us show that the cryptosystem Cr using a pseudorandom generator as g is secure in the sense of this definition. Assume the opposite, i.e., let there exist a polynomial time probabilistic algorithm A and a polynomial p such that $Pr \geq 1/2 + 1/p(n)$ for infinitely many values of n. Consider the algorithm B which gets a binary string r of length $q(n)$ as an input, chooses $m \in_R \{0, 1\}^{q(n)}$, computes $d = m \oplus r$ and calls A as a subroutine with d as the input. After receiving a pair (i, σ) from A the algorithm B checks whether indeed $m_i = \sigma$, produces 1 if the statement is true, 0 otherwise, and stops. It is easy to see that B requires polynomial time (in n). Now we can verify that B distinguishes between pseudorandom strings generated by g and random strings of length $q(n)$. Indeed, if the input strings r of B are random, then the distribution of the cryptogram d coincides with that in Cr, and therefore, by assumption, $Pr \geq 1/2 + 1/p(n)$ for infinitely many n. This contradicts the definition of a pseudorandom generator and proves that Cr is secure.

The assumption that plaintexts are picked uniformly at random is rather unrealistic. But we used it only for the sake of simplicity. One can prove the security of the cryptosystem Cr in more general settings as well. It is interesting to consider e.g. the following one. The adversary knows beforehand that one of the messages $m_1, m_2 \in$

$\{0,1\}^{q(n)}$ will be transmitted, each with probability $1/2$. His task is to guess which one, after seeing the ciphertext d. We leave it to the reader as an exercise to prove the security of the cryptosystem Cr in this setting (to this end, Definition 3 must be modified).

Of course, there are different ways to define the security of a cryptosystem with a secret key. For example, we may consider security against an attack with the choice of the public key: the adversary has an opportunity to choose in advance a polynomial number of plaintexts and get their encrypted versions; afterwards he gets the ciphertext and tries to compute at least one bit of the corresponding plaintext. It is easy to show that the cryptosystem Cr with a pseudorandom generator used for g is secure against the attack with the plaintext choice as well.

Thus we showed that pseudorandom generators allow us to construct secure cryptosystems. The main direction of research here is the construction of efficient pseudorandom generators based on various cryptographic assumptions. The efficiency is measured by the number of operations required to compute each subsequent bit of the pseudorandom sequence.

5. Zero-knowledge proofs

Suppose Alice knows a proof of some theorem, and she wishes to convince Bob that the theorem is true. Of course, Alice can simply give the proof to Bob for verification. But then Bob will be able to prove the theorem to other people himself, not referring to Alice. Is there a way for Alice to convince Bob that she knows the proof without any hint about what the proof actually is? The protocols with zero knowledge satisfy these two, apparently contradictory, requirements. These protocols were introduced by Goldwasser, Micali, and Rackoff [33] in 1989.

They considered the following model. Suppose Alice and Bob have probabilistic Turing machines $\mathbf{P}$ and $\mathbf{V}$, respectively, in their disposal. The computational resources of Alice are unlimited, while the machine $\mathbf{V}$ is polynomial time. The machines $\mathbf{P}$ and $\mathbf{V}$ can exchange messages through a common communication tape. After writing a message on the communication tape, the machine gets into the waiting state, which it leaves after the answer is written on the tape. In addition, the machines $\mathbf{P}$ and $\mathbf{V}$ have a common input tape, where the input word x is written. Alice proves the statement "$x \in L$", where L is a fixed language known to both Alice and Bob. In order to avoid trivial cases, the language L must be complicated, e.g., it may be NP-complete; otherwise Bob would be able to prove that $x \in L$ by himself. Essentially, the proof protocol consists of Bob's random questions, Alice's answers, and Bob's verification that the answers are correct. The protocol stops when the machine $\mathbf{V}$ stops; it produces 1 if the proof is accepted and 0 otherwise.

Let A and B be two probabilistic Turing machines interacting through a common communication tape. We denote by $[B(x), A(x)]$ the random output of the machine A after the machines A and B work on an input word x, and by $|x|$ the length of the word x.

Definition 4. An *interactive proof for a language L* is a pair $(\mathbf{P}, \mathbf{V})$ of interacting Turing machines such that the following two conditions are satisfied.

1 (Completeness). For each $x \in L$ we have

$$\Pr\{[\mathbf{P}(x), \mathbf{V}(x)] = 1\} = 1.$$

2 (Correctness). For each Turing machine $\mathbf{P}^*$, every polynomial p, and any word $x \notin L$ of sufficiently large length we have

$$\Pr\{[\mathbf{P}^*(x), \mathbf{V}(x)] = 1\} < 1/p(|x|).$$

The completeness property means that if the input word belongs to the language L and both Alice and Bob follow the protocol, then the proof is always accepted. The correctness requirement protects Bob from possible Alice's dishonesty in case Alice tries to deceive Bob and to prove a false statement. In this case Alice may deviate from the protocol in any possible way, i.e., she can use an arbitrary Turing machine $\mathbf{P}^*$ instead of $\mathbf{P}$. The requirement guarantees that the probability of a successful trick is negligible.

Definition 5. An interactive proof protocol for a language L is called a *zero-knowledge proof* if, in addition to conditions 1 and 2 in the previous definition, it satisfies one more condition:

3 (Zero-knowledge property). For any polynomial time proba-bilistic Turing machine $\mathbf{V}^*$ there exists a probabilistic Turing machine $\mathbf{M}_{\mathbf{V}^*}$ running in expected polynomial time in $|x|$ and such that for all $x \in L$ we have

$$\mathbf{M}_{\mathbf{V}^*}(x) = [\mathbf{P}(x), \mathbf{V}^*(x)].$$

The machine $\mathbf{M}_{\mathbf{V}^*}$ is called a simulating machine for $\mathbf{V}^*$. The average working time is expected to be bounded by a polynomial in $|x|$. This means that $\mathbf{M}_{\mathbf{V}^*}$ can work for a rather long time depending on the values of the random variables it uses. However, the probability that this time will exceed some polynomial bound is low. For each machine $\mathbf{V}^*$, its own simulating machine must be constructed; it can use the machine $\mathbf{V}^*$ as a subroutine. We denote by $\mathbf{M}_{\mathbf{V}^*}(x)$ the random output of the machine $\mathbf{M}_{\mathbf{V}^*}$ on the input word x.

The zero-knowledge property protects Alice from possible Bob's dishonesty in case Bob tries to get additional information by devi-ating from the protocol, that is, using another machine $\mathbf{V}^*$ instead of $\mathbf{V}$. Condition 3 means that in this way Bob can obtain only the information he would be able to compute himself in polynomial time without using the protocol.

Consider as an example the zero-knowledge protocol for the GRAPH ISOMORPHISM language suggested by Goldreich, Micali, and Wigderson [**35**]. An input word consists of a pair of graphs $G_1 = (U, E_1)$ and $G_0 = (U, E_0)$. Here U is the set of graph vertices, which can be identified with the set $\{1, \ldots, n\}$, and E_0 and E_1 are the sets of edges such that $|E_1| = |E_0| = m$. Two graphs G_1 and G_0 are *isomorphic* if there exists a permutation φ of the set U such that $(u, v) \in E_0$ if and only if $(\varphi(u), \varphi(v)) \in E_1$ (in this case we write $G_1 = \varphi G_0$). The problem of graph isomorphism recognition is a well-known mathematical problem, and up to now no polynomial solution for it is known. On the other hand, it is not known whether this problem is NP-complete, although there is solid evidence that it is not.

GI protocol. Let φ denote an isomorphism between G_1 and G_0. The cycle below is iterated m times; the random values used in the iterations are independent.

1. The machine $\mathbf{P}$ chooses a random permutation π on the set U, computes $H = \pi G_1$ and sends the graph H to $\mathbf{V}$.

2. The machine $\mathbf{V}$ generates a random bit α and sends it to $\mathbf{P}$.

3. If $\alpha = 1$, then $\mathbf{P}$ sends the permutation π to $\mathbf{V}$; otherwise it sends the permutation $\pi \circ \varphi$.

4. If the permutation received by $\mathbf{V}$ is not an isomorphism between G_α and H, then $\mathbf{V}$ rejects the proof and stops. Otherwise the cycle is repeated.

If the verification result of Round 4 was positive in all m iterations, then the machine $\mathbf{V}$ accepts the proof.

Note that if the machine $\mathbf{P}$ gets the isomorphism φ as an additional input word, then it does not require unlimited computational resources to implement the protocol. Moreover, in this case $\mathbf{P}$ can be a polynomial time probabilistic Turing machine.

Theorem 2 (see [**35**]). *The protocol GI is a zero-knowledge proof for the GRAPH ISOMORPHISM language.*

The completeness of the GI protocol is obvious.

In order to prove that the protocol is correct, it suffices to note that the bit α generated by the machine $\mathbf{V}$ in Round 2 tells the machine $\mathbf{P}$ which of the two graphs, G_0 or G_1, should be proved to be isomorphic to H. If G_0 and G_1 are not isomorphic, then H may be isomorphic to at most one of them. In this case, the verification of Round 4 gives a positive result with probability $\leq 1/2$, which leads to the probability $\leq 1/2^m$ after m iterations.

The proof of the zero-knowledge property is much more complicated. Therefore, we present only the main idea. Note first that the main goal of the machine $\mathbf{V}^*$ consists in obtaining as much information about the isomorphism between G_0 and G_1 as possible. It is natural to assume that, in contrast to $\mathbf{V}$, its output will consist not of a single bit, but of all the information obtained as the result of the protocol implementation, including the contents of its random tape, the graph H of Step 1, and the permutation of Step 3. The simulating machine $\mathbf{M_{V^*}}$ must be able to produce the same random strings, graphs and permutations, and it is assumed that the permutation φ

is unknown to it! Therefore, $\mathbf{M_{V^*}}$ tries to guess the bit α generated by the machine $\mathbf{V}^*$ in Round 2. In order to do this, $\mathbf{M_{V^*}}$ generates a random bit β, a random permutation ψ, and computes $H = \psi G_\beta$. Then $\mathbf{M_{V^*}}$ saves the state of the machine $\mathbf{V}^*$ (including the contents of the random tape) and calls $\mathbf{V}^*$ as a subroutine feeding it with the graph H. The machine $\mathbf{V}^*$ returns some bit α. If $\alpha = \beta$, then this iteration of simulation is successful, since $\mathbf{M_{V^*}}$ is able to demonstrate the required isomorphism. If $\alpha \neq \beta$, then $\mathbf{M_{V^*}}$ restores the state of $\mathbf{V}^*$ saved before and repeats the attempt.

If we weaken the requirement that the random values $\mathbf{M_{V^*}}(x)$ and $[\mathbf{P}(x), \mathbf{V}^*(x)]$ in the definition of zero knowledge are equal and require instead that their probability distributions be "almost equal", then we obtain another class of proofs, *statistical zero-knowledge proofs*.

One more class consists of *computational zero-knowledge proofs*. In this case we require that the model machine would produce a probability distribution that cannot be distinguished from $[\mathbf{P}(x), \mathbf{V}^*(x)]$ by a polynomial time probabilistic algorithm (the meaning of the term "distinguish" is similar to that in the definition of a pseudorandom generator).

We emphasize that in all three definitions of zero knowledge the conditions are posed only on the simulating machine behavior on words belonging to the language under consideration.

Zero-knowledge proofs are interesting not only as nontrivial mathematical objects. Their applications are also important. Identification protocols form the most natural and important kind of these applications (see Chapter 3). By such a protocol, Alice can prove her authentication to Bob.

Suppose, for example, that Alice is a smart bank card with implemented algorithm $\mathbf{P}$, and Bob is a bank computer executing the program $\mathbf{V}$. Before starting the execution of a bank operation the bank should be convinced that the bank card is authentic and identify its owner, or, in the language of cryptography, the card must pass an authentication procedure. In principle, the GI protocol above fits this purpose. In this case the bank computer memory contains a pair of graphs (G_0, G_1) assigned to Alice, and the smart card contains the same pair of graphs and the isomorphism φ. It is assumed that nobody except Alice (and, possibly, Bob) knows this isomorphism, whence the GI protocol allows the card to prove its authenticity. The completeness property implies that the card will always prove its authenticity. The correctness property protects the bank from an intruder that tries to pass the authentication procedure under the name of Alice after tampering with one or more authentication protocols of the card. Of course, in this case it makes no sense to prove that the pair of graphs (G_0, G_1) belongs to the GRAPH ISOMORPHISM language, since it is chosen from the language. Instead, Alice proves that she knows an isomorphism φ. Interactive proofs of this kind are called *knowledge proofs*.

From the point of view of applications, an important property of the GI protocol, as well as other knowledge proof protocols, is that the algorithm **P** having φ as an additional input is polynomial in time. Any other zero-knowledge protocol having the algorithm **P** possessing this property is also applicable. However, in practice the GI protocol and other protocols of this type are not efficient because of the large number of iterations, very long messages, and so on. Researchers' efforts concentrate on the search for efficient provably secure protocols.

Chapter 3

Cryptographic Protocols

1. Introduction

The subject of mathematical cryptography is information encrypting, that is, cryptosystems. In the classical model of a secret data transmission, due to Shannon, there are two partners trusting each other, who intend to exchange information not meant to be available to other persons. Such information is called confidential, or secret. The *information privacy* task thus arises. This is the first task of cryptography, at least from the historical point of view. Traditionally, it is solved by means of cryptosystems.

Let us imagine the following situation. Let A and B be two users of a communication network, say, a computer network. Suppose B is a bank where A has an account, and A wants to transmit through the network an order for the bank to pay, say, 10 sickles[1] to another customer C. Does such an operation require cryptographic protection? We suggest that the reader think about the situation and see that the protection is really necessary. However, we must emphasize an important feature of the situation: neither A nor B has any confidential information. Indeed, money orders of bank customers contain standard and public information. The bank must be sure that the message was indeed sent by A, and the customer must be sure that

---

[1] A fictitious monetary unit (see J. K. Rowling's *Harry Potter* series).

nobody can change the amount of money in his order, or send a forged payment order under his name. In other words, the communication process requires a guarantee that messages are received from an authorized source and contain genuine information. Such guarantee is called *information integrity*, and to reach it is the second task of cryptography.

It is also easy to see that sending money orders in electronic form causes yet another kind of security threat: anyone tapping into the message from A to B will know that C has got 10 sickles from A. And what if this information will be available to mafia? Probably some of the readers will suggest that here we need privacy, but they will be wrong! In fact, customers need something similar to the anonymity of usual cash: although each bill has a unique number, there is almost no way to trace who and when made a payment with it. The cryptography counterpart of this property is called *untraceability*. The untraceability implementation is the third task of cryptography.

The privacy task is usually performed by means of a cryptosystem, while the integrity and the untraceability are usually implemented by means of cryptographic protocols. Cryptographic protocols differ from cryptosystems in some other aspects as well:

– protocols can be interactive, that is, they can involve several information exchanges;

– protocols can involve more than two parties;

– generally speaking, the users of a protocol do not trust each other. Therefore, cryptographic protocols must protect the parties not only from an outside adversary, but also from unfair actions of other parties.

Unfortunately, the notion of a cryptographic protocol hardly admits formalization. The integrity and the untraceability tasks seem to possess the same property. A protocol (not necessarily a cryptographic one) is usually understood as a distributed algorithm, i.e., a collection of algorithms, one for each task, together with specifications of message formats, of synchronization, and of actions in the case of system failure. The last entry of this list requires a special attention since it is often neglected, and an inconsistent recovering procedure can destroy even a secure cryptographic protocol.

Cryptographic protocols form a rather young area of mathematical cryptography. The first protocols appeared about 20 years ago. Since then, the area enjoyed a rapid development, and by now more than two dozen various types of cryptographic protocols are known. All these protocols can be roughly separated into two groups: application protocols and primitive protocols. An application protocol solves a specific problem that occurs (or may occur) in practice. Primitive protocols form "units" in construction of application protocols.

During the last decade, cryptographic protocols became the main subject of study in theoretical cryptography. For example, the majority of talks at the largest international annual cryptographic conferences *CRYPTO* and *EUROCRYPT* are devoted to protocols. Of course, this can simply reflect the current trends of the research. But there are also objective indications that cryptographic protocols became the main object of cryptographic study. The example above shows that modern bank payment systems use electronic payment instead of the traditional one. The benefit of this innovation is so appreciable that it is unlikely that banks will stop using it in spite of serious difficulties (related, first of all, to integrity). And payment orders is only one kind of business documents. In addition, there are state and social documents, legal documents, and so on. All document flows in industrialized countries now tend to be electronic. We are not going to discuss the advantages and consequences of these changes. An important point for us here is that this transformation necessitates the implementation of integrity and untraceability, and therefore, the development of the corresponding cryptographic protocols in each specific case.

The discussion above contradicts the common opinion that since cryptographers managed to construct cryptosystems resisting all attacks for a long period of time, further mathematical studies in cryptography are only of academic interest. Not mentioning here cryptosystem problems, we merely note that only few first steps have been taken in the study of many types of cryptographic protocols, and a great number of mathematical problems are to be solved before cryptographic protocols will be universally used.

The main goal of the present chapter is to introduce some types of cryptographic protocols and to describe mathematical problems arising in the study of their security. We assume that the reader is already acquainted with Chapters 1, 2, and 4.

2. Integrity. Authentication and electronic signature protocols

> The mother-goat going out to the pasture warned her kid: "Baa, don't let a soul in till I get back and don't open the gate to anyone ... ."
>
> Then she locked the gate securely and went off to the pasture. No sooner was she out of sight than a wolf appeared, came to the gate and imitating the mother-goat asked the kid to open the gate. The kidlet peeped through a crack in the wall and when he saw the wolf, he cried, "Baa, you can't fool me! I know the sound of my mother's voice. ... you may go home for I won't open the gate to anyone, baa!"
>
> *The Wolf and the Kid*, Æsop's fable
>
> Then the wolf forced the blacksmith to forge him a new throat. When the goat left the house again the wolf came to the house and imitated the goat once more in a thin voice. The kid opened the door and the wolf ate him.
>
> *The Wolf and the Kid*, Russian folk tale

As we have already mentioned in the introduction, the notion of information integrity hardly admits a suitable mathematical formalization. In the present section we study integrity protection methods implemented in the most important and commonly used types of cryptographic protocols, namely, the authentication schemes and the electronic signature.

The aim and the core of authentication protocols (also called identification protocols) can be easily understood from the following example. Suppose we have an information system which uses a computer network and provides access to some data. The system administrator has the list of all users of the system, as well as the set of permissions for each of them; the permissions are used to control the access to system resources. Some users are allowed only to read certain parts of data, others can change the data. The integrity implementation in this setting consists in preventing access to the system of those who are not system users, as well as unauthorized usage of system information by the users. The most commonly used tool, the password protection, has many weaknesses. We are not going to describe them since this subject is discussed in many texts devoted to computer security. Instead, we pass directly to the cryptographic task setting.

There are two participants in a protocol: Alice, who tries to prove her authenticity, and Bob, who must verify this authenticity. Alice has two keys: an open public key K_1, and a secret key K_2. Alice must prove that she knows K_2 in such a way that the proof could be verified by a person who knows only the public key K_1.

The authentication problem was already discussed in Chapter 2. The basic requirements a secure authentication protocol must satisfy were also discussed there. Recall that a zero-knowledge proof protocol satisfies the requirements. In Chapter 2, we described a zero-knowledge proof protocol for the GRAPH ISOMORPHISM problem. However, from the practical point of view, this protocol has too many rounds of message exchanges between Alice and Bob.

Below, we describe one of the most efficient, from the practical point of view, protocols due to Schnorr [58]. Its description requires some additional notation, which will also be used later in this chapter.

Let p and q be prime numbers such that $p - 1$ is divisible by q. Schnorr [58] suggests that p should be of binary length close to 512, while q of binary length close to 140. Take $g \in \mathbb{Z}_p$ such that $g^q = 1 \mod p$, $g \neq 1$. Let $x \in \mathbb{Z}_p$, and let $y = g^x \mod p$. The problem of computing x provided that y is known and p, q and g are given is called the discrete logarithm problem (see Chapter 4). No efficient

algorithms for solving this problem are known. This is the base for
the conjecture of intractability of the discrete logarithm problem. Let
us state it more precisely. Let n be a growing integer parameter, and
suppose p is chosen from the set of all primes of length n such that
$p-1$ has a prime factor of length at least n^ε for some constant $\varepsilon > 0$,
q belongs to the set of all such prime divisors of $p-1$, and we have
$g^q = 1 \bmod p$, and $x \in \mathbb{Z}_q$. Then $f(x,p,q,g) = (g^x \bmod p, p, q, g)$ is
a one-way function; see Chapter 2. Schnorr's suggestions concerning
the binary length of the numbers p and q can be interpreted as follows.
At the time Schnorr's paper was published (1989) the inversion of
the function f was considered infeasible for p of length 512 and q
of length 140, respectively. Note, however, that both the hardware
development and the progress in the algorithmic number theory (see
Chapter 4) may lead to the necessity to increase these numbers.

For a secret key of the authentication scheme Alice chooses a
random value x from the set $\{1, \ldots, q-1\}$. Then Alice computes
the public key $y = g^{-x} \bmod p$ and publicizes it. The public keys
of all participants of the scheme must be publicized in a way that
prevents the opportunity to change the key (such depository of keys
is called a certified public directory). The authenticity of public keys
is a separate problem, and we do not study it in the present chapter.

Schnorr's authentication scheme.

1. Alice chooses a random number k from the set $\{1, \ldots, q-1\}$,
computes $r = g^k \bmod p$ and sends r to Bob.

2. Bob chooses a random query e from the set $\{0, \ldots, 2^t - 1\}$,
where t is a parameter, and sends e to Alice.

3. Alice computes $s = (k + xe) \bmod q$ and sends s to Bob.

4. Bob verifies the relation $r = g^s y^e \bmod p$; he accepts the proof
if the relation is satisfied, and he rejects it otherwise.

We emphasize that, in contrast to the proof protocol for the
GRAPH ISOMORPHISM problem, where the number of rounds (that
is, message exchanges between Alice and Bob) grows with the increasing length of the input (the number of vertices in the graph),
the number of rounds in Schnorr's algorithm is 3, independently of

the values of other parameters. Therefore, from the practical point of view, Schnorr's algorithm is much more efficient.

The first requirement to the authentication protocol security, the soundness, means that an adversary knowing only the public key can pass the authentication only with negligible probability. A simple analysis shows that the soundness of Schnorr's protocol depends on the chosen value of t. Indeed, if t is small, then the adversary can simply guess the query e that he will receive from Bob in the second round. Suppose for simplicity that $t = 1$. Then an adversary, who does not know the secret key x, can act as follows. Tossing up a fair coin, he chooses one of the values 0 or 1 with equal probability. Denote this value by e'. Then the adversary chooses an arbitrary element s from the set $\{0, \ldots, q-1\}$, computes $r = g^s y^{e'} \bmod p$ and sends r to Bob. It is clear that the query e Bob will send in the second round will coincide with e' with probability $1/2$. This is exactly the probability of an adversary to pass the authentication procedure.

However, if t is sufficiently large, then the probability to guess the query e successfully is low. Schnorr [**58**] recommends $t = 72$. Of course, the probability of a successful simple guess, which equals 2^{-72}, is negligible. But what if an adversary attacks the scheme using more sophisticated tools? The goal of the theoretical cryptography consists precisely in the study of the security of cryptographic schemes against all possible (efficient) attacks.

If, in Schnorr's scheme, Alice is the adversary, then she can choose r in an arbitrary (but efficient) way. In other words, Alice uses a polynomial time probabilistic algorithm that computes for each specific value of r the probability of choosing this r.

Let r be a value sent by Alice to Bob in the first round. Suppose we managed to find two queries $e_1, e_2 \in \{0, \ldots, 2^t - 1\}$, $e_1 \neq e_2$, such that the corresponding values of s found by Alice both give the positive result. Denote these values by s_1 and s_2, respectively. We have

$$r = g^{s_1} y^{e_1} \bmod p,$$
$$r = g^{s_2} y^{e_2} \bmod p.$$

Hence,

$$g^{s_1} y^{e_1} = g^{s_2} y^{e_2} \bmod p,$$

or

$$g^{s_1 - s_2} = y^{e_2 - e_1} \bmod p.$$

Since $e_1 \neq e_2$, the element $(e_2 - e_1)^{-1} \bmod q$ exists, and

$$(s_1 - s_2)(e_2 - e_1)^{-1}$$

is the discrete logarithm of y, i.e., $(s_1 - s_2)(e_2 - e_1)^{-1} = x \bmod q$.

Thus, one of the following possibilities takes place:

• either pairs of queries e_1, e_2, $e_1 \neq e_2$ such that Alice gives a correct answer for both of them (for a given r) are rare enough, and in this case the probability of successful Alice's attack is negligible; or

• such pairs are "rather frequent", and then Alice's algorithm can be used for computing discrete logarithms.

Schnorr [**58**] used this informal idea to prove that the discrete logarithm problem reduces polynomially to the problem a passive adversary faces, that is, an adversary who tries to pass the authentication procedure knowing only the public key. In other words, he proved that if the discrete logarithm problem is hard, then Schnorr's authentication scheme is secure against a passive adversary, i.e., the scheme is sound.

Note that, in contrast to a widely spread opinion, similarly to other statements of the same kind in theoretical cryptography, this result is not asymptotic by nature: if the discrete logarithm problem is hard for numbers p and q of a given length, then Schnorr's scheme is sound when using numbers of this length.

An active adversary can pass through a number of sessions of this protocol checking honest proofs (or tamper with such verification procedures) and then try to attack the authentication scheme. For a scheme to be secure against an active adversary, it suffices that the authentication proof protocol be a zero-knowledge proof. However, nobody has yet proved the zero-knowledge property for Schnorr's scheme. Moreover, the only way to prove the zero-knowledge property presently known is the so-called "black box" method. In this approach the simulating machine uses the verification algorithm (the Turing machine V^*, in notation of Chapter 2) only as an oracle, that is, feeding it with an arbitrary input without analyzing its structure, and getting the output. Goldreich and Krawczyk [**31**] proved that a three-round zero-knowledge proof, where the zero-knowledge property is established by the "black box" method, exists only in the trivial case, i.e., if the verifier himself can check the statement without the help of the prover. For Schnorr's scheme, this means that either there is no efficient algorithm for discrete logarithm computation, or the zero-knowledge property of the protocol cannot be proved by the "black box" method. The existence of zero-knowledge proofs such that this property cannot be established by the "black box" method remains an open problem.

It is easy to show that Schnorr's scheme possesses a slightly weaker property: the zero-knowledge property with respect to an honest verifier. In this case, it is sufficient to construct a simulating machine only for an honest verifier that indeed chooses a random query e from the set $\{0, \ldots, 2^t - 1\}$.

The only information Bob receives as a result of the protocol execution is the triple of numbers (r, e, s) such that $r = g^s y^e \bmod p$ and $r \neq 1$. Denote the set of all such triples by Ω. In such a triple the element e is chosen uniformly at random in the set $\{0, \ldots, 2^t - 1\}$, and $r = g^k \bmod p$, where k is a random element of the set $\{1, \ldots, q - 1\}$. It is clear that under such choice of k the value r is uniformly distributed among all nonunit elements of the group generated by g. The value of s is computed according to Round 3 of the protocol, and it is uniquely determined by the values e and r. Thus, the probability distribution on the set Ω is determined by the random choice of e and k.

A simulating machine must implement on the set Ω a probability distribution coinciding with that in the protocol. However, the machine cannot use the formula from Round 3 since this formula involves the secret key x. Instead, the simulating machine chooses random e and s from the sets $\{0, \ldots, 2^t - 1\}$ and $\{0, \ldots, q - 1\}$, respectively, and computes $r = g^s y^e \bmod p$. If $r = 1$, then the attempt fails and a new pair (e, s) is generated; otherwise the simulating machine produces the triple (r, e, s) as the output. Recall that the simulating machine is constructed only under the assumption that the prover is honest. This means, in particular, that the public key y belongs to the group generated by g, i.e., there is a number $x \in \{1, \ldots, q - 1\}$ such that $g^{-x} = y \bmod p$. Then it follows that the element $r = g^s y^e = g^s g^{-xe} = g^{s-xe} \bmod p$ also belongs to this group for any e and s. It remains to note that since the simulating machine chooses s randomly and independently of e, the value $(s - xe) \bmod q$ also is a random element of the set $\{0, \ldots, q - 1\}$ independent of e. Therefore, the number r generated by the simulating machine is a random element of the group generated by g, and this element is independent of e; hence, its distribution coincides with that in the protocol. In other words, there are two ways to create the same probability distribution on the set Ω: we can either choose a random k (and therefore, r) and compute $s = (k + xe) \bmod q$, or choose a random s and take $r = g^{s-xe} \bmod p$.

The zero-knowledge property with respect to an honest prover can prove to be satisfactory if the authentication scheme is used, for example, to control the entrance in a guarded building. In this case Alice is a smart identity card, and Bob is the guard computer. The main problem in this situation is the correctness of the authentication scheme, and there is no reason to protect oneself from a dishonest verifier. Concerning the zero-knowledge property with respect to an honest verifier, it becomes important, since it protects from an adversary trying to tamper with the protocol transactions trying to develop a false identity card.

An example of an authentication protocol is given in the epigraph to the present section. In this protocol the mother-goat plays the role of a prover, and the kid is the verifier. The aim of the protocol is to defend the integrity of the kid. An attack on the protocol also is described. The wolf is the adversary, and he is an active adversary: he starts with overhearing the protocol implementation, and then tries to pass the authentication procedure as a prover (the goat). During this process he collects some information. The protocol happened to be not secure against the active adversary. The goat should have consulted professional cryptographers and used, for example, the Schnorr scheme.

Before completing the discussion of authentication protocols, we must emphasize that no property of a cryptographic protocol, even if rigorously proved, can guarantee its security in everyday usage. Indeed, even a zero-knowledge proof protocol does not protect from the following attack on the identification scheme, which is known in cryptography literature as the "mafia threat". There are four participants, A, B, C, and D in this script. Suppose A orders a cup of coffee in a cafe, and pays with a bank card. The execution of any bank operation requires a card identification procedure, i.e., an authentication protocol execution. But B, the owner of the cafe, is a criminal, and at the very same moment C, his accomplice, tries to buy a diamond ring in a store belonging to a jeweler D. The card reading device of B and the identity card of C are special read-and-transmit devices designed for transmitting messages between A and D. As a result, A identifies himself to D instead of interchanging messages with B.

We are not going to discuss here the practical aspects of the "mafia threat". It is given only as an example demonstrating that a mathematically rigorous proof that a cryptography protocol is secure is not sufficient by itself. An application of a specific protocol requires also a detailed analysis of the environment where it is implemented; such analysis can be done by experts in information security.

Now we are going to discuss another kind of authentication protocols, the electronic signature protocols. These protocols guarantee message authentication; that is, they certify that a message is received from an authorized user and the message itself is not corrupted. Moreover, the integrity here has a more extended meaning: the addressee is not only assured that the message came from an authorized user, but he also gets an electronic signature, which can be used to convince the third party (a judge) if the sender would try to call his signature off. The electronic signature is absolutely similar to the handwritten signature on a piece of paper; the only difference is that a judge usually is a technical expert who certifies the authenticity of the signature. The role of the expert is similar to that of the graphologist in a usual arbitration. In the introduction we have already discussed, using the example of payment orders, the general purpose of electronic signature schemes.

Electronic signature protocols designed for practical use are always noninteractive (i.e., the message exchange consists in sending a single signed message to an addressee). This is a result of the efficiency requirements.

As usual, in a mathematical model we regard an electronic signature scheme as an infinite family of schemes depending on an integer parameter n, $n > 0$; this parameter is called the security parameter.

An electronic signature scheme is a triple of algorithms (G, S, V), where

- G is a probabilistic polynomial time key generating algorithm. Fed with the sequence 1^n, the algorithm G produces a pair (K_1, K_2), where K_1 is the public key of the signature scheme, and K_2 is the corresponding secret key. The key K_1 is publicized in a public certified directory;

- S is a probabilistic polynomial time signature generating algorithm. Fed with a pair (m, K_2), where m is a message, the algorithm S produces a signature s for the message m;

- V is a polynomial time signature verification algorithm. If $V(K_1, m, s) = 1$, then the signature s for the message m is accepted. In this case we say that s is a valid signature for the message m. If $V(K_1, m, s) = 0$, then the signature s is rejected. If a signature s is generated on the key K_2 by means of the algorithm S, then we must always have $V(K_1, m, s) = 1$.

Here K_1, K_2, m, and s are binary strings with lengths bounded by some fixed polynomials in n.

In order to define the security of an electronic signature scheme, we must adopt some assumptions concerning the adversary. The latter can try to simulate signatures knowing only the public key of the scheme. Such adversary is called a *passive adversary*, and this is the weakest possible type of adversaries since the public key of a signature scheme is always free-for-all. Of course, a passive adversary, as well as any other person, is supposed to know the description of the signature scheme since the algorithms G, S, and V are public.

A more sophisticated adversary can try to gather some additional information about the signature scheme by collecting a certain number of pairs (*a message, a signature*). Two main possibilities exist. In an attack with known messages, the adversary intercepts a number (bounded by some fixed polynomial in n) of signed messages. The adversary has no impact on the choice of the messages themselves. Such an adversary is essentially a passive adversary since signed messages are usually transmitted through a public communication line (some papers on theoretical cryptography use a mathematical model where signed messages are published).

A more advanced adversary can himself produce messages and obtain in some way valid signatures for them. Such an attack is called a chosen-message attack, and the adversary is called *active*. We do not discuss here the possibility to establish such an attack in practice, noting only that such a possibility cannot be eliminated, and, as everywhere in theoretical cryptography, we make an assumption to the advantage of the adversary. This means that we investigate the security of electronic signature schemes against the strongest possible adversary.

In addition to an attack, we must also consider what is the threat to the security of an electronic signature scheme against which we plan to protect the scheme. The strongest threat is the total crack, that is, the situation where the adversary discovers the secret key K_2. It is clear that if this threat can be realized, then the scheme is insecure. On the other hand, it is clear that even if a scheme is secure against the total crack, from the practical point of view it is not sufficient to regard it as secure. Indeed, consider the following degenerate scheme. The algorithm G chooses a random secret key K_2 and computes $K_1 = f(K_2)$, where f is some one-way function. The algorithm S computes the signature $s = g(m)$ for a message m by means of some function g, which is easily computable. The function g is publicized as a part of the public key, and the signature verification consists in computing $g(m)$ and comparing s with the result. It is clear that this scheme is secure against a total crack since the computation of the secret key K_2 requires the inversion of the one-way function f. However, everybody can compute the signature for an arbitrary message. This example is also instructive because there are many papers in cryptography where the authors replace the required analysis of security with speculations about how hard it is to crack the system.

The weakest possible threat is the threat of *existential forgery*. Such a threat occurs if after attacking an electronic signature scheme the adversary can forge the signature of at least one, maybe meaningless, message.

The security of an electronic signature scheme is defined with respect to a pair (*an attack, a threat*). The most secure schemes are those that are secure against the weakest threat resulting from the strongest attack, that is, against the existential forgery on the base of the chosen-message attack. Let us describe this attack and this threat more rigorously. A systematic description of attacks on electronic signature schemes and threats for them can be found in [**34**].

By an adversary, we mean a probabilistic Turing machine A that receives the string 1^n and K_1 as the input and completes its work in polynomial (in n) time. The signature generating algorithm S (which knows the secret key K_2) serves as an oracle for the machine A. Hence, A can choose messages $m_1, \ldots, m_l$, where $l \leq p(n)$ for some polynomial p, and get valid signatures $s_1, \ldots, s_l$ for them. When estimating the running time of the machine A, each query to the oracle is viewed as a single command. We may assume that when choosing the message m_i, the machine A knows already the signatures $s_1, \ldots, s_{i-1}$ for all previous messages. Such an attack is called adaptive. After the attack the machine A must find a pair (m, s) such that $m \neq m_i$ for all $i = 1, \ldots, l$ and s is a correct signature for the message m. Denote by $A(1^n, K_1) \rightarrow (m, s)$ the event consisting in finding such a pair. An electronic signature scheme (G, S, V) is called secure against the existential forgery based on an (adaptive) chosen-message attack if for any Turing machine A of the above kind, for any polynomial P, and for all sufficiently large n we have

$$\Pr\{A(1^n, K_1) \to (m, s)\} < 1/P(n).$$

Here the probability is determined by the random parameters of the algorithms G, S and A.

An easy argument similar to that used in Chapter 2 shows that the existence of electronic signature schemes secure against existential forgery on the base of a chosen-message attack requires the existence of one-way functions. One of the most remarkable achievements of theoretical cryptography is the proof of the fact that this condition is also sufficient. This result is rather nontrivial, so we present only the idea of the proof.

We start with the electronic signature scheme suggested by Lamport [51]. Let $f : \Sigma^n \to \Sigma^n$, where $\Sigma = \{0, 1\}$, be a one-way function. Denote by Σ^r the set from which the messages to be signed are chosen (in other words, we view each message $m = m_1 \ldots m_r$ as an r-bit string). The algorithm computing the function f is public.

The key generating algorithm chooses randomly $2r$ strings x_1^0, x_1^1, $x_2^0, x_2^1, \ldots, x_r^0, x_r^1$ from Σ^n. This set of strings forms the secret key of the signature scheme. Then the algorithm computes the values

$$y_1^0 = f(x_1^0), y_1^1 = f(x_1^1), \ldots, y_r^0 = f(x_r^0), y_r^1 = f(x_r^1).$$

The set of strings $y_1^0, y_1^1, \ldots, y_r^0, y_r^1$ is publicized as the public key of the scheme.

The signature for a message $m = m_1 \ldots m_r$ is the sequence of strings $(x_1^{m_1}, \ldots, x_r^{m_r})$. In other words, the ith element of the signature coincides with x_i^0 or x_i^1 depending on whether the ith bit of the message is 0 or 1. The verification procedure for the signature $S = (s_1, \ldots, s_r)$ is obvious: one simply computes the values $f(s_i)$ and compares the results with the corresponding strings $y_i^{m_i}$ of the public key.

Lamport's scheme is one-time; it allows one to sign a single r-bit message, and then new keys should be generated, and the public key in the certified directory should be changed. But this scheme possesses the required security property: if f is a one-way function, then the scheme is secure. Indeed, suppose $Y = (y_1^0, y_1^1, \ldots, y_r^0, y_r^1)$

is the public key, and (m, s) is a message and the valid signature for
it, which is computed on a secret key $X = (x_1^0, x_1^1, \ldots, x_r^0, x_r^1)$ corresponding to the public key Y. Suppose the adversary can find in
polynomial time, with probability at least $1/P(n)$ for some polynomial P, a pair (m', s'), where $m' \neq m$ and s' is the valid signature
for m'. Denote by i_0 the index of the bit where the messages m and
m' are distinct; suppose for definiteness that $m_{i_0} = 0$ and $m_{i_0}' = 1$.
Then the signature s does not contain the substring $x_{i_0}^1$, and s' must
contain a substring x such that $f(x) = y_{i_0}^1 = f(x_{i_0}^1)$. Therefore, the
algorithm A used by the adversary for computing s' must be capable
of inverting the function f for the given value y_{i_0}. Then the following
algorithm contradicts the assumption that f is a one-way function.
Suppose u is chosen randomly from Σ^n, and $v = f(u)$ is given as
the input. Choose a random j from the set $\{1, \ldots, 2r\}$. For each
$i = 1, \ldots, 2r$, $i \neq j$ generate the corresponding components of the
keys X and Y by means of the algorithm G, and substitute v for the
jth element of the key Y. Then we call the algorithm A feeding it
with the key Y. When A queries the oracle about the signature for
some message m, we check whether a preimage of v is required to sign
the message. If the answer is "yes", then the attempt fails (the probability of this event is $1/2$). Otherwise we generate the signature s
for m and give it to A.

If A forges the signature for some message m', $m' \neq m$, successfully, then we verify whether this signature does contain a preimage
of v. If this is the case, then we output this preimage.

It is clear that in the case of success this algorithm inverts the
function f. Moreover, it works in polynomial time. Now let us estimate the probability of success. Note first of all that the input for
the algorithm A is the public key Y, and the probability distribution
on the set of all possible values of Y coincides with that in the case
where A attacks the signature scheme. Therefore, we guess the values
i_0 and m_{i_0}' successfully (i.e., the event $j = 2 \cdot i_0 + m_{i_0}'$ occurs) with
probability $1/2r$. Then the total probability of the successful event
is at least $1/4rP(n)$, that is, at least $1/Q(n)$ for some polynomial
Q (recall that, by definition, r is at most polynomial in the security
parameter n).

Let us mention that if in the Lamport scheme we allow any message of length at most r (and not only messages of length precisely r) to be signed, then knowing the signature for a message m we easily construct the signature for any head of the message m. For example, from the signature to the message "trespassing is prosecuted" we can easily produce the signature for the message "trespassing". Of course, there are simple and efficient ways to protect the message. For example, we may require short messages be padded by zeroes up to length r. However, this curious situation illustrates well the following general principle: stating that a cryptographic scheme is secure one must specify precisely the values of all parameters; it often happens that even a small modification of specified values destroys the security completely.

Now the only problem is to make Lamport's scheme reusable. The idea of such transformation is obvious: when signing a current message m we must choose a new public key Y and the new secret key X, and send the addressee the triple (m, Y, s), where s is the signature for the concatenated message $m\|Y$. As a result, we obtain a sequence $Y_1, Y_2, \ldots, Y_j, \ldots$ of public keys and a sequence of the corresponding signatures $s_2, \ldots, s_j, \ldots$. Here Y_1 is the public key from the certified directory, and s_j is the signature for the public key Y_j generated by using the secret key X_{j-1} corresponding to the public key Y_{j-1}. Thus, each public key Y_j will be authenticated through the sequence of signatures $s_2, \ldots, s_j$, and therefore, it can be used together with the secret key X to generate signatures and to verify their correctness. However, the following serious problem arises: each pair of keys (X, Y) allows one to sign only one message of length r, while the length of the public key is $2rn$ bits.

To describe a way of solving this problem we need a new notion, that of *cryptographic hash function*. A hash function is a rather interesting cryptographic notion, and it deserves a more detailed discussion. Here we only give a brief description. Informally, a hash function is a relatively easily computable function compressing input values and such that there is no efficient way of finding collisions. A collision for a hash function h is a pair of values x, y, $x \neq y$, such that $h(x) = h(y)$. Since a hash function contracts input values, collisions are unavoidable, but they can be found by the exhaustive search. However, by definition, there is no algorithm that can find collisions for a cryptographic hash function in polynomial time.

The following definition of a family of one-way hash functions was given by Naor and Yung in [**51**]. Let n be an integer parameter, $n > 0$, and let H_n be a set of functions $h : \Sigma^n \to \Sigma^k$, where $k = k(n) < n$. We assume that $n < p(k)$ for some polynomial p. For each function $h \in H_n$ a description $\bar{h}$ is given, and there is a polynomial time probabilistic algorithm that produces, for the input 1^n, a description from the set of all descriptions of functions in H_n chosen uniformly at random. We also assume that there is a polynomial time algorithm which generates the value $h(x)$ from an input $x \in \Sigma^n$ and the description $\bar{h}$ of the function h. The adversary, who tries to find collisions, is a polynomial probabilistic algorithm B running in two stages. On the first stage it gets 1^n as the input and produces some value $x \in \Sigma^n$. Afterwards, B gets a description $\bar{h}$ chosen randomly from the set of all descriptions of functions from H_n. The family $\{H_n\}$ is called a family of one-way hash functions if for any such algorithm B, any polynomial P, and all sufficiently large n we have

$$\Pr\{B(\bar{h}) = y \mid y \in \Sigma^n, y \neq x \& h(x) = h(y)\} < 1/P(n).$$

Suppose there is a family of one-way hash functions $\{H_{2nr}\}$, where $H_{2nr} = \{h : \Sigma^{2nr} \to \Sigma^k, k < n\}$. Naor and Yung [**51**] showed that there is the following way to make Lamport's scheme reusable employing such a family. The signer chooses a random description $\bar{h}$ of a function $h \in H_{2nr}$ and puts this description into the certified directory together with the public key Y_1. The length of messages to be signed is $n - k$. When the first message is signed, a new pair of keys (X_2, Y_2) is generated and the value $h(Y_2)$ is computed. Then the message is signed using the first $n - k$ elements of the key X_1, and the value $h(Y_2)$ is signed using the last k elements. After that, the message, the new public key, and the signatures are sent to the addressee. Further messages are signed in a similar way. The verification of the signature consists either in verification of the entire chain starting from Y_1, or requires saving the last public key authenticated by the signer.

The analysis of this scheme (see details in [**51**]) shows that in order to forge signatures the adversary must know either how to substitute the public key Y_j without changing the value $h(Y_j)$, that is, to find collisions for the function h, or how to invert the function f.

It remains to understand why the possibility to find collisions contradicts the definition of a family of one-way functions. Indeed, the adversary knows the description $\bar{h}$ in advance, and he gets the value for which the collision must be found afterwards; therefore, the task the adversary faces when attacking the signature scheme seems to be easier than that in the definition of a family of one-way functions. However, the signer chooses $\bar{h}$ and all X_j independently and uniformly at random. Therefore, all Y_j are also independent of $\bar{h}$. Hence, an adversary attacking the hash function can choose the key Y in the same way the signer does and obtain a random description $\bar{h}$. It is clear that this does not increase the probability of a successful attack.

Naor and Yung [**51**] constructed a family of one-way hash functions under the assumption that there exists a one-way permutation. Rompel [**57**] strengthened their result by showing that the existence of an (arbitrary) one-way function is sufficient. Thus, he proved that electronic signature schemes that are secure against existential forgery based on a chosen-message attack, exist if and only if there are one-way functions.

This fundamental result can be interpreted as follows. If there are signature schemes secure in some, possibly very weak, sense, then there are schemes secure against existential forgery based on a chosen-message attack, i.e., schemes that are secure in the strongest possible sense. Indeed, as was mentioned above, if a signature scheme can be considered secure in some sense, then it must be secure against the total break, and the latter statement implies the existence of one-way functions.

Unfortunately, in practice this signature scheme is very inefficient and cannot be used. First of all, the signatures are prohibitively long. Each bit in a signed message requires n bits of the signature. Secondly, the addressee must store all public keys starting from Y_1 and the whole sequence of signed messages in order to be able to show them to the judge in case arbitration is needed. There are some methods of shortening the sequences as well as the length of signatures, but there is no way to get rid of this weakness completely. The problem of whether the assumption of the existence of a one-way function allows one to construct efficient electronic signature schemes remains open.

Now let us investigate an example of an efficient electronic signature scheme. Recall Schnorr's authentication scheme. The interaction in this protocol is used only to get a random query e from the verifier. Therefore, if the prover would have a reliable probability generator enjoying the confidence of the verifier, then it would be possible to make the protocol noninteractive. Fiat and Shamir [**28**] suggested that the authentication protocol be converted into an electronic signature scheme by substituting some "surrogate" for the random query. Namely, let m be the signed message, and let h be a cryptographic hash function. Then instead of querying the verifier (that is, the addressee), the prover (that is, the signer) computes the value $h(m)$ and uses it as the query e. This method is universal: it can be applied to a wide class of authentication protocols. Now let us describe the electronic signature scheme due to Schnorr [**58**], obtained in this way. Here the public and the secret key of the signer are generated in the same way as in Schnorr's authentication scheme. The public key is publicized in the public certified directory.

Schnorr's electronic signature scheme.

1. The signer chooses a random $k \in \{1, \ldots, q-1\}$ and computes the value $r = g^k \bmod p$.

2. The signer computes $e = h(r, m)$, where m is the signed message.

3. The signer computes $s = (k + xe) \bmod q$ and sends the addressee the message m with the signature (e, s).

4. The verifier computes $r' = g^s y^e \bmod p$ and checks the equality $e = h(r', m)$. If the latter is true, then the signature is approved; otherwise it is rejected.

We assume that the hash function h takes pairs (m, s) to elements of the set $\{0, \ldots, 2^t - 1\}$.

It is easy to verify that the signature generated by means of this protocol will always be approved in Round 4.

The security level of Schnorr's scheme is essentially determined by the properties of the function h. If the adversary can find collisions of a special form, i.e., if he can find, for a given pair (r, m), another message m', $m' \neq m$ such that $h(r, m') = h(r, m)$, then he can existentially forge signatures. In order to do this it suffices to tap into a message m together with the signature (e, s) for this message and to find a collision of the above form. Then the pair (e, s) also will be a signature for the message m'.

Hash functions constitute an essential part of electronic signature schemes. This results from the necessity to sign messages of variable length. Of course, one can split a long message into blocks of fixed length required by the signature scheme and sign each block separately, but this solution is inefficient. In practice, hash functions taking messages of arbitrary length to hash values of required length are used. It is clear that such a hash function must be, in some sense, secure against attempts to find collisions. Unfortunately, hash functions are constructed in practice for specific lengths of hash values (say, 256 bits), and there is no way to formalize this requirement.

In contrast to the situation with authentication protocols, we know no ways of proving security for practical electronic signature schemes. Secure signature schemes cannot be zero-knowledge proofs. This fact is easy to understand if we recall that the definition of zero knowledge requires the existence of a simulating machine, which produces, for the values observable by the verifier, the same probability distribution as in the protocol execution without knowing the secret key. But during the protocol execution the verifier (that is, the addressee) sees only messages with signatures. Therefore, a simulating machine, if it exists, should be able to forge signatures, since the "signatures" it generates must be indistinguishable from the genuine ones; in particular, they cannot be distinguished from the genuine signatures by the signature verification algorithm.

The security of electronic signature schemes against a passive adversary who tries to forge signatures knowing only the public key may be proved in the so-called *random oracle model*. In this model, the signer and the addressee, instead of computing the function h, call an oracle who produces for each input value α a random output value β. The oracle stores the pair (α, β), and any further call with the same input value α again results in the output value β. Fiat and Shamir [28] noted that the idea of proving the soundness of authentication schemes above can be applied to prove the security of signature schemes against a passive adversary. This statement holds for a wide class of signature schemes including Schnorr's scheme. In fact, this means that signature schemes are secure (against a passive adversary described above) if the behavior of the hash function is similar to that of a random function. This statement is essentially the only result in theoretical cryptography concerning the security of practical electronic signature schemes. We should mention, however, the paper [61], where the same statement is proved under the assumption that the behavior of the hash function is similar to that of a decryption function in a secure (in some sense) cryptosystem.

3. Untraceability. Electronic money

> And he causeth all, both small and great, rich and poor, free and bond, to receive a mark in their right hand, or in their foreheads:
>
> And that no man might buy or sell, save that he had the mark, or the name of the beast, or the number of his name.
>
> Here is the wisdom. Let him that hath understanding count the number of the beast: for it is the number of a man; and his number *is* Six hundred threescore *and* six.
>
> *The Revelation of St. John the Divine*

About fifteen years ago, residents in some parts of Moscow found unusual letters in their mailboxes. Written by rather illiterate people on pieces of paper taken from school notebooks, these letters contained the same drudgingly rewritten text about (keeping the original terminology) a "confuter", called "The Beast", which appeared somewhere in Bruxelles (in NATO headquarters perhaps?), and whose serial number is 666. And this "confuter" allegedly assigned a number to each human being on the Earth, and without this number nobody can buy or sell, or do anything at all. Of course, in conclusion, the early Judgement Day was predicted.

These letters, as well as all the others of the same kind, would not be worth mentioning had the authors not touched, without knowing it, a serious problem: a threat for human rights and civil liberties that the development of computers brings to people.

Since the present section is devoted to electronic money, let us consider this threat using the following simple example. A credit card, which is widely spread and popular in the modern society, is a data medium producing a complete identification of its owner at each payment transaction. If the owner of the card uses it to buy tickets, then all his moves can be traced, and this situation must be impossible in the present world without prosecutor's approval. Similarly, one can collect information about each owner of a credit card concerning goods he buys, cultural events he visits, and so on.

But further developments will lead to even worse situations. Computer access to information databases and the storage of all documents in the electronic form will produce the background for tracing all facets of each person's life. Of course, this list of threats can be extended.[2] In conclusion, we may say that the development of computers opens opportunities for watching everybody to the extent impossible before. What makes the threat more serious is that even experts have not fully recognized it yet.

For protection against this threat we need a system of controlling the access to resources that would satisfy two, apparently contradictory, requirements. First of all, the system must produce an anonymous access to the resource for each person, and secondly, each person must prove his right to use the resource. Usual cash has both properties. If the resource is some goods, and the customer has enough cash to buy an article, then this cash proves his right to access the resource. On the other hand, although each bill carries a unique number, it is

---

[2]When the present section has already been written, the issue of "Computerra" magazine (no. 20, May 20, 1998) appeared, where these threats are discussed in more detail. Note that one of the authors also had associations with the words from the Revelation quoted in the epigraph to this section.

impossible, in practice, to trace it by the number. On the other hand, credit cards satisfy only the second requirement.

In what follows, by electronic money we mean electronic payment facilities that guarantee untraceability. Similarly to the notion of integrity, the notion of untraceability can hardly be formalized, and we shall explain it by examples of specific protocols.

The electronic payment protocols are special cryptographic protocols to process money. Three parties participate in these protocols; we call them the bank, the buyer, and the seller. Both the buyer and the seller have an account in the bank, and the buyer wishes to pay the seller for an article or a service.

There are three main transactions in the payment system:

– withdrawal;

– payment;

– deposit.

In a withdrawal transaction the buyer gets an electronic bill (we will call it e-bill, or simply bill) from the bank containing the required amount; the bill must be signed by the bank. The bank account decreases in value by the withdrawn amount. In a payment transaction the buyer transmits a note to the seller and indicates the payment sum. The seller transmits this information to the bank, and the latter verifies the authenticity of the note. If the bill is authentic, then the bank verifies whether it has been utilized before. If not, then the bank increases seller's account by the required amount of money, notifies the seller about this event, and, if the denomination of the bill is greater than the payment sum, returns the remainder to the buyer (through the seller). The buyer puts the "change" to his account through a deposit transaction.

The bank is secure because it is impossible to forge its signature and to produce a false bill, or in a more general setting, it is impossible, having a set of authentic e-bills, to forge the bank signature on at least one new e-bill. The buyer is untraceable if the bank cannot identify the payer of the bill it receives in a payment transaction, and the same concerns the "change". This, seemingly self-contradictory, requirement can be satisfied by means of the scheme of so-called black-out (blind) signature: in the withdrawal the bank signs, in fact, not a bill, but some "abracadabra", and the buyer reconstructs the bill from the signed abracadabra. Hence the untraceability is reached due to the fact that the bank simply does not know what it has signed.

Consider the simplest version of a payment system using a black-out signature corresponding to the RSA signature scheme. The latter is based on the principle similar to that of the RSA cryptosystem (see Chapter 4). The signer (the bank, in our case) chooses two secret sufficiently large prime numbers p and q and publicizes their product $N = pq$. Let e and d, where $ed = 1 \bmod \varphi(N)$, be the public and the secret key, respectively, of the RSA cryptosystem. In the RSA electronic signature scheme, the signature generating procedure consists in applying the decryption function $s = m^d \bmod N$ of the RSA cryptosystem to the message m. In order to check the signature, one must apply the encryption function to it. If $s^e = m \bmod N$, then s is the valid signature for the message m.

Now, the bank chooses and publicizes the numbers N and e, as well as some one-way function $f : \mathbb{Z}_N \to \mathbb{Z}_N$ (the role of this function will be described later). The bank uses the pair of keys (e, d) only for producing e-bills; i.e., all parties agree that the electronic signature generated by using a key d corresponds to the e-bill of denomination, say, 1 sickle.

In a withdrawal transaction the buyer chooses a random number $n \in \mathbb{Z}_N$ and computes $f(n)$. The only thing he needs is the bank signature on this bill, that is, the value $f(n)^d$. However, the buyer cannot simply transmit the value $f(n)$ to the bank, since he must identify himself to the bank in order to withdraw from the account. Therefore, receiving $f(n)$ the bank will always be able to trace the bill, and the untraceability requirement fails. A solution to this problem consists in using a blackout signature: the buyer chooses a random value $r \in_R \mathbb{Z}_N$, $r \neq 0$, computes $f(n)r^e \bmod N$, and sends the resulting value to the bank. The factor r^e is often called the blackout factor. The bank computes the number $f(n)^d \cdot r \bmod N$ and returns it to the buyer. The buyer easily removes the blackout factor and receives, as the result, a signed bill $(n, f(n)^d \bmod N)$.

In a payment transaction the buyer transmits to the seller the
e-bill $(n, f(n)^d \bmod N)$. In principle, the seller can verify the authenticity of each bill (n, s) himself. In order to do this, it suffices
to compute $f(n)$ and to verify that $f(n) = s^e \bmod N$. However,
an e-bill, as well as any other computer data, can be easily copied.
Therefore, a dishonest buyer can pay with one bill many times. In
order to avoid this threat, the seller transmits the bill to the bank,
and the latter checks, through a special register, whether it was used
before. If not, then the bank transfers 1 sickle to the seller's account
and sends a notification to the seller.

In this payment scheme, the bank security is based on our be-
lief in the RSA electronic signature scheme security. The necessity
of the function f in this construction is explained by the well-known
multiplicativity property of the RSA scheme: if s_1 and s_2 are the signatures for m_1 and m_2, respectively, then $s_1 s_2 = m_1^d m_2^d \bmod N$ is the
signature for $m_1 m_2$. Therefore, if the electronic payment system used
bills of the form $(n, n^d \bmod N)$, one would be able to produce a third
authentic bill from two authentic bills at his disposal. The customers'
untraceability in this system is absolute. The only information the
bank gets about an account withdrawal is the value $f(n)^d \cdot r \bmod N$,
which is, due to the blackout factor r, simply a random number from
$\mathbb{Z}_N$. Therefore, the bank has no information about the bill it transfers
to the customer.

In the above example the bank gives only bills of denomination
1 sickle, and all payments are multiples of this one. It turns out that
also a more flexible scheme is realizable. Consider the electronic payment system suggested in [15]. By the way, all main ideas related to
the untraceability property, electronic money, and blackout signature
schemes belong to the author of that paper, a Dutch mathematician
D. Chaum.

The system suggested in [15] also is based on the RSA electronic
signature scheme. By some abuse of notation, we write "$n^{1/t} \bmod N$"
instead of "$n^d \bmod N$, where $dt = 1 \bmod \varphi(N)$", and we call this
number the root of n of degree t. As above, the function $f : \mathbb{Z}_N \to \mathbb{Z}_N$
is a one-way function chosen and publicized by the bank.

Let us agree that the root of degree equal to the ith odd prime number corresponds to the denomination of 2^{i-1} sickles. This means that the bearer of a pair $(n, f(n)^{1/3} \bmod N)$ is an owner of an e-bill of denomination 1 sickle. If the root of degree 7 is substituted here for the root of degree 3, then the denomination of the bill is 4 sickles, whereas the root of degree 21 corresponds to the 5-sickle bill. In other words, a bill of denomination S requires a root of degree equal to the product of all prime numbers corresponding to the digits 1 in the binary representation of S.

All bills produced by the bank have the same denomination. For simplicity we assume, following [15], that they are 15-sickle bills. Then the bank's signature on a bill is the root of degree $h = 3 \cdot 5 \cdot 7 \cdot 11$. The scheme requires also an additional RSA-module N_1, which is used in operating the cookie jar. This module is chosen and publicized in the same way as the module N.

A withdrawal transaction proceeds in the same way. As a result, the buyer gets an e-bill of denomination $(n_1, f(n_1)^{1/h} \bmod N)$.

Now suppose that the buyer wants to pay the seller 5 sickles. In order to do this he computes $f(n_1)^{\frac{1}{3 \cdot 7}} \bmod N$ by simply computing the 55th degree of the bill, and creates a cookie jar by choosing a random value j and computing $f(j)s_1^{5 \cdot 11} \bmod N_1$. Here once again $s_1^{5 \cdot 11}$ is the blackout factor. The payment transaction starts with transmitting the seller the data n_1, $f(n_1)^{\frac{1}{3 \cdot 7}} \bmod N$, $f(j)s_1^{5 \cdot 11} \bmod N_1$, as well as the payment amount (5 sickles). The seller transmits this information to the bank. The bank easily verifies that the pair $(n_1, f(n_1)^{\frac{1}{3 \cdot 7}})$ is an authentic bill of denomination 5 sickles. It checks through a special register whether the bill with the number n_1 was used earlier. If not, then the number of the bill is written in the register, the bank increases seller's account by 5 sickles, and sends the seller the confirmation and "change" (10 sickles), which is returned through the cookie jar $f(j)^{\frac{1}{5 \cdot 11}} s_1 \bmod N_1$.

In the deposit transaction the buyer transmits to the bank the cookie jar $(j, f(j)^{\frac{1}{5 \cdot 11}})$. The bank verifies its authenticity in the same way as it was done for the bill in the payment transaction, and if the cookie jar with the number j is authentic and was not used in a deposit transaction earlier, then the bank credits 10 sickles to the buyer's account.

If all payments are made in the maximal possible amount (15 sickles), then the scheme guarantees perfect (information-theoretic) untraceability of the buyer: the blackout signed by the bank retains no information about the number of the signed bill.

The need to deposit the change received from the bank destroys the untraceability: the bank stores all payments and hence all change, and it can, therefore, trace a customer if his payment amount was unique or sufficiently rare. A partial solution to this problem consists in the multishot use of the cookie jar in payment transactions.

Suppose the buyer received another bill, numbered n_2, from the bank and wishes to pay 3 sickles to the same or a different seller. Then he can use the cookie jar containing the change remained after the first payment transaction and transmit the data n_2, $f(n_2)^{\frac{1}{3 \cdot 5}} \bmod N$, $f(j)^{\frac{1}{5 \cdot 11}} s_2^{7 \cdot 11} \bmod N_1$ to the seller. The payment transaction proceeds in the same way as above, and as a result the buyer gets the cookie jar containing $f(j)^{\frac{1}{5 \cdot 11 \cdot 7 \cdot 11}} \bmod N_1$ sickles.

During the deposit, the buyer transmits to the bank the values j, $f(j)^{\frac{1}{5 \cdot 7 \cdot 11 \cdot 11}} \bmod N_1$ and indicates the required amount. The bank verifies the cookie jar in the same way it did for the bill, that is, it checks the existence of all roots of degrees specified by the buyer, and it also checks that the cookie jar with number j has not been used in any previous deposit transaction. If all these conditions are satisfied, then the bank credits the contents of the cookie jar to buyers' account.

If the number of customers in the bank system is large enough and if each of them uses a single cookie jar until the amount of money in the jar exceeds a fixed limit (say, 100 sickles), then the chances of the bank to trace the activities of a single customer seem to be negligible.

Both examples considered above belong to the class of so-called centralized systems which is characterized by the requirement that the bank participates in all payment transactions. Autonomous electronic payment systems, where the seller can verify the authenticity of electronic money received from the buyer by himself, are much more efficient. To distinguish the autonomous systems from the centralized ones, we will talk about *electronic coins* (there is no standard term here).

As we have mentioned above, there is no way to prevent repeated usage of an electronic coin without calling the bank. Instead, autonomous systems identify a violator *post factum*. Constructions of autonomous systems are rather complicated (see, e.g., [**66, 13**]). Here we describe briefly only the main idea. Our description is based on Schnorr's authentication scheme, but any other scheme possessing all required properties is also applicable.

Each customer of the bank chooses a secret key x containing the customer's identification; then he computes the public key $y = g^x \bmod p$. In a withdrawal transaction the customer chooses a random value of k and computes $r = g^k \bmod p$. An electronic coin is a string containing y and r and the bank signature for this string. The main problem here is that the bank must sign the coin by a blackout signature, but it must be sure that the structure of the coin is correct. An interested reader can find a solution to this problem in [**13**].

In a payment transaction the seller first verifies the signature of the bank, and if it is valid, then, similarly to Schnorr's authentication scheme, chooses a random query e and sends e to the buyer. The latter computes $s = (k + ex) \bmod q$ and sends s to the seller. The seller verifies the validity of the answer using the values r and y contained in the coin.

In a deposit transaction, the seller transmits the electronic coin to the bank together with e and s. If the bank discovers that the coin received was already used, then there are two distinct pairs (e, s) and (e', s') satisfying the verification test in Schnorr's scheme for the same values y and r. As was shown in the previous section, it is sufficient for the bank to compute the secret key x and therefore identify the violator.

A remarkable property of autonomous systems is that, on one hand, they guarantee the untraceability of honest customers, and on the other hand, they allow an unambiguous identification of violators. But using such a system means a risk to the bank, since there may be not enough money on the violator's account to settle the debt at the moment the second payment is discovered. This problem is discussed in more detail in [5].

In the majority of autonomous systems an electronic coin can be used only once, and then the deposit transaction must be executed. If a coin can be used for multiple payments without intermediate deposits, then such a coin is called *transferable*. If transferable coins were used for sufficiently long time, the customers' payments would become practically untraceable. But in this case it would become a much more complicated task to discover multiple payments by means of the same coin. One more weakness is the increasing length of the coin with each use. From the intuitive point of view this seems natural since the coin must contain the information that allows identification of a violator who spent the coin twice. Therefore, each user of the coin must leave a kind of "fingerprints" on it. Chaum and Pedersen [16] proved that the increase of coin's length is, in fact, inevitable.

4. Coin flipping by telephone protocols

> "Very well; but first hand me over the money."
>
> "The money? I have it here. Do you write out the receipt, and then the money shall be yours."
>
> "Pardon me, but how am I to write out the receipt before I have seen the cash?"
>
> Chichikov placed the notes in Sobakevitch's hand; whereupon the host moved nearer to the table, and added to the list of serfs a note that he had received for the peasants therewith sold, the sum of twenty-five roubles, an earnest money."
>
> N. V. Gogol', *Dead Souls*
> Translated by D. J. Hogarth

In the present section we briefly discuss cryptographic protocols allowing two parties to exchange information by telephone. The participants of the protocol do not trust each other, and each of them may prove to be a liar. Therefore, if a participant of the protocol let some information out too early, then he may receive in return either not the expected information, or no information at all: the tasks here are the same as in the "protocol" of exchanging bills and the receipt between Chichikov and Sobakevitch.

Perhaps the most impressive protocol of this kind is the coin flipping protocol (it is also rather simple). Suppose that two participants, Alice and Bob, must draw lots. If they are in the same place, then the problem can be solved by the usual coin flipping procedure. If one of the participants does not trust the coin, then other sources of randomness can be used. Let us mention that constructing reliable sources of randomness is a rather nontrivial problem; it belongs, however, to statistics, not to cryptography.

If Alice and Bob are at different places and can communicate only via some communication line, then, at the first sight, the lots drawing problem seems unsolvable. Indeed, if Alice following the usual procedure chooses one of the two possible results (heads or tails), then Bob can always declare the result that is beneficial to him.

Nevertheless, Blum [11] solved this problem. Curiously enough, even the title of the paper refers to "solving impossible problems".

It is clear that if there were a trustworthy agent (a third party) who enjoys confidence of both Alice and Bob and has secure (private) communication lines with both participants, the problem would have a very simple solution. In this case Bob and Alice simply choose random bits b and c, respectively, and send them to the agent in secrecy. The latter waits until he receives both bits, and then publicizes b, c, and $d = b \oplus c$, which is the coin flipping result.

If there is no trustworthy agent, then the following idea works (we describe here its simplest physical implementation). Bob chooses a random bit b, writes it on a piece of paper, locks the piece in a box, and sends the box to Alice keeping the key. It is assumed that Alice cannot open the box without the key. After receiving the box Alice chooses a random bit c and sends it to Bob. In return, Bob sends Alice the key. The result of the coin flipping is the bit $d = b \oplus c$ as above.

Below, we explain the cryptographic implementation of the same idea based on the discrete logarithm problem. We preserve the notation of Section 2.

Coin flipping protocol.

1. Alice chooses a random value $x \in_R \mathbb{Z}_q$, computes $y = g^x \bmod p$ and sends y to Bob.

2. Bob chooses a random bit b, a random value $k \in \mathbb{Z}_q$, computes $r = y^b g^k \bmod p$ and sends r to Alice.

3. Alice chooses a random bit c and sends it to Bob.

4. Bob sends b and k to Alice.

5. Alice checks whether the equality $r = y^b g^k \bmod p$ holds. If yes, then the result is the bit $d = b \oplus c$.

The number r is the cryptographic counterpart of the box from the physical implementation. Indeed, knowing r Alice can extract no information about the bit b. Since k is chosen from $\mathbb{Z}_q$ in a random way, r is a random element of the group generated by g for both $b = 0$ and $b = 1$, and therefore, it carries no information about b (of course, Alice can try to cheat and choose y not belonging to the group generated by g; however, Bob easily discovers that by verifying the equality $y^q = 1 \bmod p$).

On the other hand, Bob also can cheat by choosing the value 0 or 1 of the bit b as he wishes; however, he can only do this if he can compute discrete logarithms. The following argument confirms this statement. Since, as was mentioned before, we can assume that r belongs to the group generated by g, there is a unique number $\alpha \in \mathbb{Z}_q$ such that $r = g^\alpha \bmod p$. In order to be able to choose the value $b = 0$ Bob must send to Alice the value α in Round 4, and in order to be able to choose $b = 1$ he must send $k = (\alpha - x) \bmod q$. Hence, $x = (\alpha - k) \bmod q$. Let M be a polynomial time probabilistic Turing machine used by Bob to implement this trick. Then the following algorithm can compute discrete logarithms.

1. Feed M with y.

2. After receiving the answer r save the state of M.

3. Choose a random bit c and transmit it to M.

4. Having received the values b and k from M save these values, restore the state of M previously saved, and go to Round 3.

5. As soon as two pairs of the form $(0, k_1)$, $(1, k_2)$ are found among the pairs (b, k), compute the value $x = (k_1 - k_2) \bmod q$, which is the discrete logarithm of y.

This argument leads to a proof of the following statement. The coin flipping protocol described above is secure provided the discrete logarithm problem is hard. Note that the security of the given protocol requires a rather weak form of this assumption. Since Alice can interrupt the protocol execution if the gap between transmitting y to Bob and receiving the answer b, k from him exceeds, say, 30 seconds, it suffices to presume that the discrete logarithm problem cannot be solved in this time interval.

If we select from the coin flipping protocol only Rounds 1, 2, and 4, then we obtain the so-called *bit commitment protocol*. Rounds 1 and 2 in this protocol are called the commitment stage, while Round 4 is the bit choosing stage. The value r in this protocol used to pack the bit b (the analogue of the box in the physical realization) is often called a *blob*; Alice is called the *recipient*, and Bob is called the *sender*. Informally speaking, a blob construction in a bit commitment protocol must possess the following two properties simultaneously:

1) after the commitment stage is completed, the receiver cannot discover which bit is packed in the blob;

2) on the bit choosing stage, the sender can choose any blob only as 0 or 1.

In our case, requirement 1) is necessarily satisfied, i.e., the receiver cannot discover the bit in the blob by himself. In this case one says that the protocol guarantees the perfect security for the sender. On the other hand, the security of the receiver is based on the unproved assumption that the discrete logarithm problem is hard. This asymmetry is typical for many types of cryptographic protocols, for example, to protocols with computably zero knowledge. However, there is another type of bit commitment protocols, where the security of the sender is perfect, while that of the receiver is based on unproved assumptions. Such dual protocols are constructed for many types of cryptographic protocols with the asymmetry as above.

Bit commitment protocols form one of the basic types of primitive cryptographic protocols. They are applied in various areas of cryptography. As an illustration, consider a way to make zero-knowledge proofs more efficient; we illustrate this by the example of the protocol for the GRAPH ISOMORPHISM problem considered in Chapter 2. The main difficulty in this protocol is the large number of rounds, which grows proportionally to the size of the graph. A rather natural idea is to process these consecutive rounds in parallel. In the first step, the machine $\mathbf{P}$ chooses m random permutations $\pi_1, \ldots, \pi_m$, computes $H_1 = \pi_1 G_1, \ldots, H_m = \pi_m G_1$ and transmits all these m graphs to $\mathbf{V}$. In the second step, the machine $\mathbf{V}$ chooses m random bits $\alpha_1, \ldots, \alpha_m$ and transmits them to $\mathbf{P}$. Finally, in the third step the machine $\mathbf{P}$ forms all the required m permutations and sends them to $\mathbf{V}$.

But is this a zero-knowledge protocol? Note first of all that the protocol consists of three rounds, and, as the result due to Goldreich and Krawczyk mentioned in Section 2 shows, presumably there are no three-round proofs with zero knowledge. The method used in Chapter 2 to construct a simulating machine worked because in the serial processing of the protocol the simulating machine can guess the query α_i of the verifier successfully with probability $1/2$. In the parallel version, the probability of a successful guess is $1/2^m$, that is, it is negligible. Besides, the verifier forms his queries $\alpha_1, \ldots, \alpha_m$ after receiving all graphs $H_1, \ldots, H_m$ from $\mathbf{P}$, and whence he can choose queries depending on the graphs in a rather complex way. This obstacle for constructing a simulating machine also seems insurmountable.

One can overcome the dependence of $\alpha_1, \ldots, \alpha_m$ on $H_1, \ldots, H_m$ in the following way. The verifier $\mathbf{V}$ chooses his queries before he sees the graphs $H_1, \ldots, H_m$. Each bit α_i is packed in a blob r_i, and $\mathbf{V}$ sends all blobs $r_1, \ldots, r_m$ to the prover. After this, $\mathbf{P}$ sends to $\mathbf{V}$ all graphs $H_1, \ldots, H_m$. Then $\mathbf{V}$ opens the blobs, and $\mathbf{P}$, after receiving the bits $\alpha_1, \ldots, \alpha_m$, forms the required permutations and sends them to $\mathbf{V}$.

As a result, the number of rounds in the protocol increases, but it remains a constant (5 rounds is enough). Using a bit commitment protocol which guarantees the perfect security of the sender, even a prover with unlimited computational power will not be able to extract any information about the queries $\alpha_1, \ldots, \alpha_m$ from the blobs $r_1, \ldots, r_m$. Therefore, the correctness of the protocol is preserved.

Now, the second obstacle above is surmounted. And what about the first? It turns out that there is no reason for the simulating machine to guess the queries of $\mathbf{V}^*$. The following remarkable idea was repeatedly used in papers devoted to cryptographic protocols (see [7]). After receiving the blobs from $\mathbf{V}^*$, the simulating machine M_{V^*} saves the state of the machine $\mathbf{V}^*$, chooses graphs $H'_1, \ldots, H'_m$ as random permutations of the graph G_0, and transmits them to $\mathbf{V}^*$. In return, $\mathbf{V}^*$ opens the blobs, and M_{V^*} receives the queries $\alpha_1, \ldots, \alpha_m$. Then the simulating machine forms graphs $H_1, \ldots, H_m$ in return to the queries $\alpha_1, \ldots, \alpha_m$, restores the state of the machine $\mathbf{V}^*$ saved earlier, and transmits $H_1, \ldots, H_m$ to the machine. Since the bit commitment protocol is assumed to be secure, the machine M_{V^*} receives the same bits $\alpha_1, \ldots, \alpha_m$ once again, and it completes the simulating process successfully by producing $\alpha_1, \ldots, \alpha_m$, $H_1, \ldots, H_m$, the contents of the random tape of the machine M^*, the required permutations, the blobs $r_1, \ldots, r_m$, and the messages generated by the machine $\mathbf{V}^*$ in order to choose them.

Now suppose that the assumption on which the security of the bit commitment protocol is based, is proved. For example, suppose somebody managed to prove that there are no polynomial time algorithms for the discrete logarithm problem. Even in this case a polynomially bounded sender in the bit commitment protocol above can guess x successfully with a small probability, which, however, is not zero. In this case the sender can deceive the receiver. As a result, the parallel version of the protocol considered above is only a statistical zero-knowledge protocol, while the original serial version (see Chapter 2) is a perfect zero-knowledge protocol. The method of transforming serial protocols into parallel ones described above was suggested in the paper [7] by Bellare, Micali, and Ostrovsky; they use a special construction of blobs for the GRAPH ISOMORPHISM problem, which preserves the perfect zero-knowledge property.

5. More about secret sharing

The following historical example is described in the paper [42] with reference to the book "Gent und seine Schönheiten" (Thill-Verlag, Bruxelles, 1990). The town tower was constructed in Gent in the 13–14th centuries. The most important documents, the charters and patents, were guarded in the "secret", most secure chamber of the tower. The chamber had two doors, each door with three locks, and each guild had a key to a lock. The documents were kept in a filing cabinet, which, in turn, was also locked with three keys. The warden had one of the keys, and the stuart, the other two.

We describe this example in the section devoted to secret sharing protocols to illustrate the fact that although cryptographic protocols are rather young, the problems they solve appeared long ago and they have their own long history.

Why is the title of the section "More about secret sharing"? In Chapter 5, secret sharing is treated as a mathematical problem, first of all a combinatorial one. Here we discuss it as a cryptographic protocol. We assume that the reader is somewhat familiar with Chapter 5.

In a secret sharing protocol, there are n parties $P_1, \ldots, P_n$, which will be called processors, and one distinguished participant D, called a dealer (or, sometimes, a leader). The protocol splits into two stages.

At the secret splitting stage, the dealer, who knows some secret s, generates n parts $s_1, \ldots, s_n$ of the secret and sends the part s_i to the processor P_i through a secure communication line. At the secret reconstruction stage, any group of at least $t+1$ processors reconstructs the secret uniquely communicating through secure communication lines (here t is a parameter of the protocol). It is supposed that no group of t or less processors can reconstruct the secret (the words "can reconstruct" will be explained later).

Similarly to other kinds of cryptographic protocols, the participants of a secret sharing protocol do not trust each other, and each of them, including the dealer, can turn out to be an adversary. Is there a way to protect honest participants in this case? Of course, a dishonest dealer can simply block the protocol execution. However, if he tries to apply a more sophisticated technique, then it is possible to protect other participants in the following way. In the beginning of the secret sharing stage the dealer publicizes the secret s in an "encrypted" form (to be more precise, he commits the string s, similarly to the bit commitment). Using this information, each processor P_i can verify that the value s_i it receives from the dealer is indeed a part of the secret s. Such protocol is usually called a *protocol of verifiable secret sharing*. In usual secret sharing schemes an adversary is assumed to be passive, i.e., it consists of at most t parties that try to get some information about the secret by combining their shares. On the secret reconstruction stage of a verifiable secret sharing protocol the adversary is assumed to be active: trying to prevent the recovery of the secret, dishonest parties of the protocol can send to the honest ones an arbitrary information rather than their shares of the secret. We require that if there are at least $t + 1$ honest parties of the protocol, then they can always reconstruct the secret.

Below, we describe a protocol of verifiable secret sharing first presented in [**27**]. The construction is based on the discrete logarithm problem. As above, p denotes a prime number, and g is an element of high order in $\mathbb{Z}_p$. Parameters p and g are publicly known. According to Shamir's scheme, the dealer chooses a random polynomial $Q(x) = a_0 + a_1 x + \cdots + a_t x^t$ of degree t, where $a_0 = s$, computes $r_i = g^{a_i} \bmod p$ ($i = 0, 1, \ldots, t$) and publicizes $r_0, \ldots, r_t$. Then the dealer computes $s_j = Q(j)$ for each $j = 1, \ldots, n$ and transmits the value s_j to the processor P_j through a secure communication line. Checking the equality

$$g^{s_j} = r_0 \cdot (r_1)^j \cdots (r_t)^{j^t} \bmod p$$

the processor P_j verifies that s_j is indeed a part of the secret g:

$$r_0 \cdot (r_1)^j \cdots (r_t)^{j^t} = g^{a_0} \cdot g^{a_1 j} \cdots g^{a_t j^t}$$
$$= g^{a_0 + a_1 j + \cdots + a_t j^t} = g^{Q(j)} \bmod p.$$

Now let us describe the protocol for the secret reconstruction stage in the easiest case where the dealer is assumed to be honest. On this stage each processor P_j sends to every other processor P_i the share s_j of the secret. Having received s_j, each honest processor checks this value as described above and rejects all shares s_j that did not pass the test. Since there are at least $t + 1$ honest parties, each processor P_i will get at least $t + 1$ correct shares of the secret. Then P_i can reconstruct s by the secret reconstruction algorithm from Shamir's scheme.

In contrast to the secret sharing schemes of Chapter 5, the security of this protocol is based on the assumption that the discrete logarithm problem is hard. Therefore, the requirement that any subset of participants not forming a quorum get no information about the secret is replaced in many schemes of verifiable secret sharing by the requirement that such a set just cannot "recover" the secret. This means that the reconstruction procedure requires a solution of a hard computational problem. In our example each participant can reconstruct the secret s provided that he can compute discrete logarithms.

One of possible applications of secret sharing schemes is cryptographic key depositories. For such applications, the verifiability property is crucial. But the area of applications of verifiable secret sharing schemes is much wider.

Suppose that the above scheme was used to share two secrets s_1 and s_2, both of which are numbers. Now suppose we need to share the secret $s_1 + s_2$. Of course, the dealer can do this by using the same protocol. But can the processors do the same without the dealer's interference?

Let $Q_1(x) = a_0 + a_1 x + \cdots + a_t x^t$ and $Q_2(x) = b_0 + b_1 x + \cdots + b_t x^t$ be two polynomials used for sharing the secrets s_1 and s_2, respectively. Set $r_i^1 = g^{a_i} \bmod p$ and $r_i^2 = g^{b_i} \bmod p$ for $i = 0, \ldots, t$. For each $j = 1, \ldots, n$ denote by $s_j^1 = Q_1(j)$ and $s_j^2 = Q_2(j)$ the shares of the secrets s_1 and s_2, respectively, received by the processor P_j. It is clear that the sum $Q(x) = Q_1(x) + Q_2(x)$ also is a polynomial of degree t and $Q(0) = s$.

Therefore, each processor P_j can compute the share s_j of the secret s simply by the formula $s_j = s_j^1 + s_j^2$. These parts are verifiable with the help of the values $r_i = r_i^1 \cdot r_i^2 \bmod p$.

Rabin and Ben-Or showed in [54] that making similar computations with shares of secrets, the processors can compute an arbitrary function over a finite field in a "verifiable way". This result concerns secure multiparty computations. A typical problem here looks as follows. We must compute the value of a function f on some set of arguments $y_1, \ldots, y_m$. Shares $x_1, \ldots, x_n$ of these values are computed by using a verifiable secret sharing scheme. At the beginning of the protocol only the processor P_i knows the part x_i. The protocol must guarantee that the value $f(x_1, \ldots, x_n) = f(y_1, \ldots, y_m)$ will be computed in such a way that, for some parameter t,

1) no subset of the set of processors consisting of less than t processors will receive any information about the values x_i in other processors (besides those borrowed from the known shares and the value $f(x_1, \ldots, x_n)$);

2) all honest parties can compute $f(x_1, \ldots, x_n)$ regardless of actions of dishonest parties provided that the number of dishonest parties does not exceed t.

Due to their generality, universal confidential computational protocols are of particular theoretical interest. Besides, many types of cryptographic protocols (say, election protocols) are essentially special kinds of secure multiparty protocols.

A number of theorems of the following kind is proved under different assumptions about the processors and the communication networks: if t is not greater than some threshold (depending on n and on the assumptions), then each computable function admits a secure multiparty computational protocol.

6. Playing building blocks, or Election protocols

> ... Le suffrage universel est une stupidité.
>
> ... Vous admettez bien avec moi que les hommes de génie sont rares, n'est-ce pas? Pour être large, convenons qu'il y en ait cinq en France, en ce moment. Ajoutons, toujour pour être large, deux cents hommes de grand talent, mille autres possédant des talents divers, et dix mille hommes supérieurs d'une façon quelconque. Viola un état-major de onze mille deux cents cinq esprits. Apres quoi vous avez l'armée des médiocres, qui suit la multitude des imbéciles.

Comme les médiocres et les imbéciles forment tou-
jours l'immense majorité, il est inadmissible qu'ils
puissent élire un gouvernement intelligent.

G. de Maupassan, *Les dimanches*
d'un bourgeois de Paris

The reader who passed through the previous sections could get an
idea that cryptographic protocols are an easy thing. This is because
we have chosen protocols that, in our opinion, are easy to understand
at the first acquaintance with the topic. Besides, the presentation
was semiformal in order to make the main ideas clear. In fact, the
majority of cryptographic protocols, and election protocols among
them, are rather complicated.

As we have already mentioned in the introduction, primitive cryptographic protocols are used as a kind of "building blocks", and protocols used in applications are assembled from these blocks. In the
present section we study the process of assembling a protocol.

Suppose there are l voters $V_1, \dots, V_l$ that are network nodes and
vote electronically. Suppose, for simplicity, that there are two possible
results of the election, "yes" or "no"; these results will be encoded
as 1 and -1, respectively. Here are the two main requirements to an
election protocol:

1) the ballot must be secret;

2) the votes must be counted correctly.

As we have mentioned in the previous section, election protocols
can be regarded as a specific form of secure multiparty computation
protocols. At the initial moment each participant V_i possesses a secret
value $b_i \in \{-1, 1\}$, his vote, and the function $f(b_1, \dots, b_l) = \sum_{i=1}^{l} b_i$
must be computed. The secure multiparty computation protocol sat-
isfies the two aforementioned requirements only if the percentage of
dishonest parties is sufficiently small. This solution has a remarkable
property: only voters participate in the protocol, and there is no need
in a coordinating center whom all voters trust. But it also possesses a
rather serious defect. Secure multiparty computation protocols are so

complicated that (from the point of view of the number of computations made by each party and the amount of transmitted information) even for sufficiently small l they are practically unrealizable.

There is another way consisting in establishing a voting center where the votes are counted (we call it simply the center). Suppose first that the center is honest and it enjoys voters' absolute confidence. In this situation the following solution works. The center chooses a secret key x and a public key y of some public key cryptosystem and publicizes y. Each voter V_i sends to the center a message containing voter's identification and the vote b_i encrypted by the public key y. The center checks the congruence of the ballots to the list of voters, decrypts the ballots, rejects invalid votes (that is, the votes not belonging to the set $\{-1, 1\}$), counts and publicizes the result.

Even this simple scheme contains a trap. If each voter simply encrypts his bit b_i using the key y, then there are only two possible cryptograms and all anonymity of the ballot is broken. It is possible, for example, to encrypt a string consisting of the bit b_i completed, say, by a random string on the right. This approach imposes some new requirements on the cryptosystem: the leading bit of the public key must be hard, i.e., the problem of reconstructing this bit from a cryptogram must be equivalent (in the sense of polynomial reducibility) to the problem of reconstructing the entire public text. Such cryptosystems exist, but the probabilistic encrypting system (see [**32**]) is better; in this system the cryptogram of a message m on a key k is computed by a randomized algorithm $c = E_k(m, r)$, where r is a random string. This means, generally speaking, that each message admits exponentially many cryptograms computed with the same key. But decryption is always unique! Probabilistic encryption systems were introduced by Goldwasser and Micali in [**32**]; they proved, under some additional assumptions, the existence of cryptosystems of this kind possessing the so-called semantic security. This is an analog of Shannon's perfect security, but with respect to adversaries working in polynomial time.

As an example, we describe a version of the El Gamal cryptosystem [**25**] based on the discrete logarithm problem. In the notation of Section 2, let G_q be the subgroup in $\mathbb{Z}_p^*$ generated by g. The private key x is picked uniformly at random in $\mathbb{Z}_q$; the public key is computed as $y = g^x \bmod p$. For a message $m \in G_q$, a value[3] $\alpha \in_R \mathbb{Z}_q$ is chosen and the cryptogram (a, b), where $a = g^\alpha \bmod p$, $b = y^\alpha m \bmod p$, is computed. The addressee, who knows the secret key x, computes

$$b/a^x = y^\alpha m/(g^\alpha)^x = y^\alpha m/g^{x\alpha} = y^\alpha m/y^\alpha = m \bmod p.$$

Now let us return to the election protocol. Let h be another generator of the group G_q. Then for $b \in \{-1, 1\}$ the ballot is computed in the form $(g^\alpha, y^\alpha h^b)$. After applying the decryption algorithm the center obtains the value $h^b \bmod p$, and it can extract the bit b simply by substituting both values 1 and -1.

In this voting scheme the ballot cannot by anonymous in principle since the center knows the ballot of each voter. But the situation with the correctness of the ballot counting is different. Suppose a scoreboard is established to store the information, and there is a row in the board for each voter. This row contains, for example, the complete identification data of the voter, and the voter puts his ballot in the same row. It is supposed that all voters, as well as other watchers, have free access to the board. After the expiration moment the board is "turned off", i.e., its current state is stored. Then each voter is given some time to verify the contents of his row on the board. Then all reclamations are considered, and the required changes are made. When all voters are satisfied, the contents of the board is finally fixed.

Then the center computes the value $z = \sum_{i=1}^{l} b_i$ and publicizes the election result z. Let $(g^{\alpha_i}, y^{\alpha_i} h^{b_i})$ be the ballot of the voter V_i. Since all ballots are on the board, all voters, as well as outsiders, can compute the pair

$$\left(\prod_{i=1}^{l} g^{\alpha_i} \bmod p, \prod_{i=1}^{l} y^{\alpha_i} h^{b_i} \bmod p \right).$$

Let us denote $A = \prod_{i=1}^{l} g^{\alpha_i} \bmod p$, $B = \prod_{i=1}^{l} y^{\alpha_i} \bmod p$. If the center computed the votes correctly, then $h^z = \prod_{i=1}^{l} h^{b_i} \bmod p$. Therefore, dividing the second element of the pair by h^z we must

---

[3]Recall that the notation "$\in_R$" means "a random element of".

obtain the value B. We set $B' = (\prod_{i=1}^{l} y^{\alpha_i} h^{b_i})/h^z \bmod p$. The problem is that the watchers do not know B and cannot verify whether $B' = B$. However, it is easy to verify the equality $B = A^x \bmod p$. Therefore, the watchers can simply demand from the center the proof of the following fact: the discrete logarithm of B' to the base A is equal to the discrete logarithm of y to the base g. Here is the protocol of Chaum and Pedersen [**17**] (cited in [**21**]) serving this purpose.

The Chaum and Pedersen protocol.

1. The prover chooses $k \in_R \mathbb{Z}_q$, computes $(\beta, \gamma) = (g^k \bmod p, A^k \bmod p)$ and sends (β, γ) to the verifier.

2. The verifier chooses a query $e \in_R \mathbb{Z}_q$ and sends e to the prover.

3. The prover computes $s = (k + ex) \bmod q$ and sends s to the verifier.

4. The verifier checks that $g^s = \beta y^e \bmod p$ and $A^s = \gamma(B')^e \bmod p$ and accepts the proof. If at least one of the equalities is false, then the proof is rejected.

The reader who studied Section 2 of this chapter can easily notice the similarity of this protocol with Schnorr's authentication scheme. We suggest that this reader analyze the security of the present protocol himself.

In principle, the center can prove the statement $B' = A^x \bmod p$ to everybody. The defect of the protocol is that it is interactive. However, using the trick that transforms the Schnorr authentication scheme into an electronic signature protocol (Section 2) it is possible to turn this protocol into a noninteractive one as well. In this case the center can simply publicize the noninteractive proof together with the result z.

Of course, the assumption that all voters trust a single ballot counting center is questionable. One can create n centers $C_1, \ldots, C_n$. Then the assumption that at least t of the n centers are honest, where, for example, $t \geq 2n/3$, seems more realistic.

In this case the centers choose together and publicize three random generators g, y, and h of the group G_q. The ballot of a voter V_i has the same form as in the version above: $(g^{\alpha_i}, y^{\alpha_i} h^{b_i})$. But now the centers are not able to decipher this cryptogram themselves. Instead, each of them computes $(\prod_{i=1}^{l} g^{\alpha_i}, \prod_{i=1}^{l} y^{\alpha_i} h^{b_i})$. The voter V_i creates shares $\alpha_{i_1}, \ldots, \alpha_{i_n}$ of the secret value α_i by the secure secret sharing scheme described in the previous section and transmits the share α_{i_j} to the center C_j. Then, processing the shares (see Section 5) the centers compute $\delta = \sum_{i=1}^{l} \alpha_i \bmod p$. If there are at least t honest centers, then neither of the values α_i can be reconstructed by other (dishonest) centers. The final result δ can be verified: the equality $g^{\delta} = \prod_{i=1}^{l} g^{\alpha_i} \bmod p$ must be satisfied. If this is the case, then δ is publicized, and this value is sufficient to compute the results of the voting. Indeed, $(\prod_{i=1}^{l} y^{\alpha_i} h^{b_i})/y^{\delta} = \prod_{i=1}^{l} h^{b_i} \bmod p$. There is yet another difficulty: in order to compute the result z we must find the discrete logarithm of the computed value. But since the absolute value of z is not too large (it is surely not greater than the total number l of voters), the discrete logarithm can be found by exhaustive search.

A new problem arises in this scheme: we must suggest a protocol for the centers to choose the generators g, y, and h together in such a way that neither of them is a known power of another. This problem admits the following solution. Let G be a probabilistic algorithm generating three random generators. It can be treated as a deterministic algorithm getting as an input not only the numbers p and q, but also a random string r of required length. The coin flipping protocol described in Section 4 can be obviously generalized to the case of n parties. Using such generalized protocol, the centers can generate the string r bit by bit (there are also more efficient schemes). The string r is random if at least one of the centers is honest. After the execution of the protocol is completed, the centers publicize r, g, y, and h. Since the algorithm G is assumed to be public, anyone who wants to verify that g, y, and h are obtained through the string r can do this.

Can we conclude that all problems are now resolved? By no means. In the case where there was one center, this center decrypted all ballots and checked their validity rejecting invalid ones. If there are many centers, then a dishonest voter can try to disrupt the election or to falsify the result. This problem can be solved if we require that each voter publicize, together with the ballot, the proof of its validity.

In other words, we require a protocol allowing a voter V_i to prove, for a given ballot (A_i, B_i), that he knows $\alpha_i \in \mathbb{Z}_q$ and $b_i \in \{-1, 1\}$ such that $A_i = g^{\alpha_i} \bmod p$, $B_i = y^{\alpha_i} h^{b_i} \bmod p$. Such a protocol must give no useful information about α_i and b_i to a verifier. An example of such a protocol is suggested in [21]; we do not describe it here because of its extreme cumbersomeness.

Are we over now? Once again, no! ... But let us stop here. We hope that now the reader is convinced that election protocols are rather nontrivial objects, and the discussion of various aspects of their implementation can last forever. Besides, we have mentioned only two main requirements for election protocols: the anonymity and the correctness of vote counting. There are many other requirements, and new ones may arise in the very analysis of electronic election protocols, where some unexpected new effects nonexistent in the present nonelectronic election schemes can be discovered. For example, in the construction of the ballot above, the voter V_i knows the values α_i and b_i, and can use these values to prove that he had voted in a specific way (say, "yes") after the elections. As a result, the votes can be bought, and this problems requires a special cryptographic solution.

For further details on election protocols see [**21, 22**], from which the above ideas concerning construction of such protocols were taken.

Now, the final note. Everywhere above we discussed (informally) only the separate security of various cryptographic primitive ingredients used in election protocols. However, a composition of secure cryptographic protocols may prove to be insecure. The study of the security of composed protocols is another, usually rather nontrivial, problem of cryptography.

7. Beyond standard assumptions. Confidential message transmission

'Can you do Addition?' the White Queen asked.
'What's one and one and one and one and one and one and one and one and one?'
'I don't know,' said Alice 'I lost count.'

'She can't do Addition,' the Red Queen inter-
rupted ...

Lewis Carroll, *Through the Looking-Glass
and what Alice Found There*

The majority of cryptographic protocols belong to one of the following two categories. The first consists of protocols that have either
information theory security, or perfect security. The second consists
of protocols whose security is based on computational hardness of
some mathematical problems. The words "is based" mean that either the protocol security is proved under some specific assumptions,
or the validity of this assumption is necessary for the security, i.e., an
adversary who managed to solve the corresponding problem efficiently
breaks the protocol.

Being a science, theoretical cryptography includes all possible
directions of research. One of these directions is the development
of cryptographic schemes that are secure under some nonstandard
assumptions. There are few papers devoted to this subject. In this
last section we describe an example of a cryptographic protocol that
is provably secure under a nonstandard assumption.

The secure message transmission problem is stated as follows.
There are two users of a communication network, Alice and Bob.
They are connected by n lines, and each line can be used to transmit
messages in both directions independently of the state of the other
lines; initially, Alice and Bob share no common secret information.
Alice has a confidential message m, and she must transmit it to Bob
securely. An active adversary, who can control at most t lines simultaneously, acts against the parties. The control over a line means that
the adversary intercepts all messages transmitted through the given
line and can replace any of them with an arbitrary other message.

If we set $n = 1$ and consider, instead of the active adversary,
a passive adversary who can only intercept the messages, then we
obtain the classical Shannon's model of secret communication. This
secure message communication problem is solved by cryptosystems.
However, cryptosystems form a separate category only by tradition.
In fact, what we need is a secure message transmission protocol. The
construction of this kind of protocol requires such components as

encryption and decryption algorithms, key sharing protocols, and so on. For example, for a public key cryptosystem a component may be an electronic signature protocol if the agency (the confidential center) that keeps the certified directory, certifies all public keys in the directory with its own signature.

If $n \geq 2t + 1$, then the following simple protocol solves the secure message transmission problem.

Note first of all that under this assumption Alice and Bob have an perfectly secure public communication line. If, for example, Alice wants to send a message x to Bob, then she sends it through all lines, and Bob chooses the value which appears at least $t + 1$ times among the n messages he receives.

Further, let q be a large prime number, $q > n$. Alice chooses a random polynomial $Q(x)$ over $\mathbb{Z}_q$, of degree t. Let $P = Q(0)$. The idea is to transmit P to Bob as a one-shot key for the Vernam cipher. The transmission must be organized in a way that does not allow the adversary to know anything about P. In order to achieve this goal, Alice uses the threshold secret sharing scheme, i.e., she sends $Q(j)$ through the jth communication line. Denote by r_j, $j = 1, \ldots, n$, the value received by Bob through the jth line. If all n pairs (j, r_j) interpolate a polynomial of degree t, then the transmission is successful and Bob can reconstruct the key P. Later, Bob and Alice communicate through the public communication line described above. If Bob receives a key P, then he notifies Alice with a special message. Then Alice computes the cryptogram $z = (P + m) \bmod q$ and sends it to Bob. Bob deciphers the cryptogram and obtains the message m. If the pairs (j, r_j) do not interpolate a polynomial of degree t, then Bob sends all the pairs to Alice, and she finds at least one j for which $r_j \neq Q(j)$. Then it is clear that the jth line is under adversary's control. Alice sends to Bob the list of all such line numbers j, and these lines are not used for further communication. Afterwards, Alice and Bob repeat the whole protocol using the remaining lines. Clearly, the transmission of the key will be successful after at most t trials.

The protocol described above is the simplest version of the secure message transmission protocol from [**24**]. A much more efficient

protocol, which is provably secure against a stronger adversary under
the same assumption $n \geq 2t + 1$, is also suggested in [24].

If the adversary is passive, i.e., if he only taps into at most t
communication lines, then the secure message transmission problem
has a very simple solution. As an easy example, we suggest that the
reader construct the corresponding protocol for $n > t$ himself.

The message transmission protocol described above is provably
secure under the assumption that the adversary does not have sufficient resources to control at least half of the communication lines
between Alice and Bob. This statement leads to the following arguments. The so-called common sense suggests that in order to construct a secret communication system, one must develop a private
communication network, that is, a communication network with restricted access. However, it seems that a really secure solution lies in
the opposite direction: we should unify all communication networks in
a common public network requiring many connections between every
two users. Of course, this is only a theoretical argument concerning
a mathematical model of real systems. The results of mathematical
cryptography, as well as of other research areas, will make us repeatedly stumble over solutions suggested by common sense.

8. In place of a conclusion

The mathematical theory of cryptographic protocols is developed by
joint efforts of scientists from different countries. The authors of papers devoted to protocols are from USA and Israel, from Canada and
Netherlands, from Italy and Japan, from France and Germany, from
Denmark and Hungary. This list can easily be extended. Only the
remarkable Russian mathematical school has almost no achievements
in this area. We hope that our readers will change the situation in
the nearest future.

Chapter 4

Algorithmic Problems of Number Theory

1. Introduction

The question on "how to compute" is one of the main questions of number theory. The works of Euclid, Diophantus, Fermat, Euler, Gauss, Chebyshev, Hermite contain ingenious and rather efficient algorithms for solving Diophantine equations, determining congruence solvability, constructing large prime numbers (large for those times), finding best approximations, and so on. Without exaggeration, one can say that number theory is threaded with algorithms.[1] During the last two decades, first of all due to the needs of cryptography and wide spread of computers, the study of algorithmic problems of number theory experience a period of exuberant and extremely fruitful development. In this chapter we describe only those algorithmic aspects of number theory that have cryptographic applications.

Computers and electronic communication lines penetrate all areas of human activities. Modern cryptography is also unimaginable without them. One can treat encryption and decryption of texts as processing integers by computers, and the methods of performing these operations, as some functions defined on integers. As a result,

---

[1]See [**68**]. (*Added in translation.*)

methods of number theory enter cryptography in a natural way. Besides, the security of some modern cryptosystems is based exclusively on the complexity of some number-theoretic problems (see [**44**]).

However, computers are not omnipotent. A long sequence of integers must be split into blocks, and each block must be encrypted separately. Below, we assume that integers to be encrypted are nonnegative and they do not exceed some specified (say, by technical restrictions) bound m. Results of encryption also satisfy the same assumptions. This means that we can treat these numbers as elements of the residue ring $\mathbb{Z}/m\mathbb{Z}$. An encryption function is then a one-to-one mapping of the residue ring $\mathbb{Z}/m\mathbb{Z}$ to itself,

$$f : \mathbb{Z}/m\mathbb{Z} \to \mathbb{Z}/m\mathbb{Z},$$

and the value $f(x)$ is the encrypted message x.

The simplest cipher of this kind is the substitution cipher corresponding to the shift $f : x \mapsto x + k \bmod m$ for some fixed integer k. A cipher of this kind was used by Julius Caesar. Of course, not every mapping f is convenient for the purposes of secure information hiding (see a more detailed discussion in Chapter 1).

In 1978, Rivest, Shamir, and Adleman [**56**] suggested an example of a function f possessing a number of remarkable properties. An encryption system widely used in practice, called RSA by the names of its authors, was constructed using this function. For this function,

a) there is an algorithm computing quickly the values $f(x)$;

b) there is an algorithm computing quickly the values $f^{-1}(x)$ of the inverse function; however,

c) there is a "secret" allowing one to compute the values $f^{-1}(x)$ of the inverse function quickly; for a person who does not know the secret, computing $f^{-1}(x)$ becomes a complicated problem from the computational point of view, and it requires so much time that after this time the encrypted information is of no interest to those who use f for encryption.

Mappings of this type and their possible applications in cryptography are described in more detail in Chapters 1, 2.

A copy of the talk in the Massachusetts Institute of Technology devoted to the RSA cryptosystem was sent to the well-known mathematical writer M. Gardner even before the paper [**56**] was published. In 1977, Gardner published in *Scientific American* the paper [**29**] describing this encryption system. The title of this paper is "*A new kind of cipher that would take millions of years to break.*" Gardner's paper played an important role in spreading information about the RSA, attracted to this cryptosystem the attention of many nonspecialists, and contributed to the rapid progress in this area during the last 20 years.

2. The RSA cryptosystem

Below we assume that the reader knows some elementary notions and facts of number theory. We refer the reader to [**63**] for the first acquaintance with these notions.

Let m and e be positive integers. The function f, which forms the base of RSA, has the form

$$(1) \qquad\qquad f : x \mapsto x^e \bmod m.$$

To decrypt the message $a = f(x)$ it suffices to solve the equation

$$(2) \qquad\qquad x^e \equiv a \bmod m.$$

Under some assumptions on m and e, the latter equation has a unique solution x.

To describe the assumptions and to explain how one can find the solution, we need a number-theoretic function called the Euler function. This is a function of a natural argument m denoted by $\varphi(m)$; its value is equal to the number of integers i, $1 \leq i \leq m$, relatively prime to m. Thus, $\varphi(1) = 1$ and $\varphi(p^r) = p^{r-1}(p-1)$ for an arbitrary prime number p and an arbitrary integer r. Besides, $\varphi(ab) = \varphi(a)\varphi(b)$ for arbitrary relatively prime integers a and b. These properties allow one to compute the value $\varphi(m)$ easily provided that the decomposition of m into the product of prime factors is known.

If the exponent e in (2) is prime to $\varphi(m)$, then (2) has a unique solution. To find it, let us find first an integer d satisfying the conditions

$$(3) \qquad de \equiv 1 \bmod \varphi(m), \quad 1 \leq d < \varphi(m).$$

Such a number d exists since $(e, \varphi(m)) = 1$, and it is unique. Here and below, we denote by (a, b) the greatest common divisor of numbers a and b. The classical theorem of Euler, see [63], says that for each number x prime to m the congruence $x^{\varphi(m)} \equiv 1 \bmod m$ holds, and therefore,

$$(4) \qquad a^d \equiv x^{de} \equiv x \bmod m.$$

Hence under the assumption $(a, m) = 1$, the only solution of (2) is

$$(5) \qquad x \equiv a^d \bmod m.$$

If we additionally assume that the prime factors of m are pairwise distinct, then (5) holds even if $(a, m) \neq 1$. Indeed, let $r = (a, m)$ and $s = m/r$. Then $\varphi(m)$ is divisible by $\varphi(s)$ and (2) implies that $(x, s) = 1$. Similarly to (4) we now easily find that $x \equiv a^d \bmod s$. Besides, $x \equiv 0 \equiv a^d \bmod r$. Since $(r, s) = 1$, the equalities we deduced imply (5).

The function (1) adopted in RSA can be computed rather efficiently. We discuss its computation below. Here we only note that the same procedure can be applied to the inverse function $f^{-1} : x \mapsto x^d \bmod m$ with the exponent d substituted for e. Thus, the function (1) possesses properties a) and b).

The only thing we must know to compute the function (1) is the numbers e and m. These numbers together form the public encryption key. But the computation of the inverse function requires the knowledge of the number d; this number is the "secret" mentioned in requirement c). It looks as if knowing m it is easy to find its prime factors, then compute $\varphi(m)$ by the known rules, and then find the required number d using (3). All these steps except the first one, can indeed be realized rather efficiently. It is the decomposition of m into prime factors which is the most laborious part of the job. No efficient algorithm for factoring integers has been found in number theory in spite of the long history of this problem and an intensive study during the last 20 years. Of course, a factor can be found by an exhaustive search through the first $\sqrt{m}$ integers. However, taking into account that there is about $2\sqrt{m} \cdot (\log m)^{-1}$ prime numbers in this segment (see [4], Chapter 5), we conclude that for m having 100 digits in decimal notation this procedure requires at least $4 \cdot 10^{42}$ divisions by primes. A rough estimate shows that it will take a computer executing million divisions per second more than 10^{35} years to complete the computation. There are more efficient factoring algorithms that do not include the exhaustive search of prime factors, but they also work too slowly. Hence, the title of Gardner's article is justified.

The authors of the RSA cryptosystem suggested that the product of two primes p and q of close size be chosen for m. Since

$$(6) \qquad \varphi(m) = \varphi(pq) = (p-1)(q-1),$$

the only restriction on the exponent e in mapping (1) is

$$(7) \qquad (e, p-1) = (e, q-1) = 1.$$

Thus, a person intending to implement in a company an encrypted correspondence scheme based on the RSA cryptosystem must choose two sufficiently large prime integers p and q. Multiplying them the person obtains the product $m = pq$. Then a number e satisfying the requirements (7) is chosen, the value $\varphi(m)$ is computed by (6), and the value d is computed by (3). The numbers m and e are published, and d remains secret. Now anybody can send messages encrypted using function (1) to the system administrator, and the latter can easily decrypt them using (5).

Rivest, Shamir, and Adleman illustrated their approach by encrypting an English phrase. First it was written in the standard numerical form ($a = 01$, $b = 02$, ... , $z = 26$, space$= 00$) as an integer x, and then encrypted using the function (1) with

$m =$114381625757888867669325779976146612010218296721242362562561842935 70693524573389730597123563958705058989075147599290026879543541

and $e = 9007$. These two numbers were published, together with the information that $m = pq$, where p and q are prime numbers having 64 and 65 digits, respectively, in the decimal notation. The award of

$100 was promised to the first person who deciphers the encrypted message

$$f(x) = 9686961375462206147714092225435588290575999112457431987469512093$$
$$0816298225145708356931476622883989628013391990551829945157815154.$$

This story was finished 17 years later in 1994, when Atkins, Graff, Lenstra, and Leyland announced in [4] the decryption of the phrase suggested in [56]. This phrase, *the magic words are squeamish ossifrage*, became the title of [4]. The corresponding factors p and q are

$$p = 24905295108476509491478496199038981334177646384933878439908 20577,$$

$$q = 3276913299326670954996198819083446141317764296799294253979 8288533.$$

The interested reader can find the details in [4]. Here we only note that this wonderful result (factoring a 129-digit decimal number) was achieved by using the factorization algorithm called the quadratic sieve method. The computations required tremendous work. After making a preliminary theoretic preparation, the four organizers put together about 600 volunteers who used about 1600 workstations communicating with each other through the Internet for about 220 days. The $100 award was assigned to the Free Software Foundation.

The RSA scheme described above brings up a number of questions which we are going to discuss. For example, how does one perform computations with large numbers? Indeed, the standard software does not allow us to multiply numbers having 65 digits in decimal notation. How is it possible to find large powers of huge numbers quickly? What is a fast algorithm and a complicated computational problem? What is the source of large prime numbers? For example, how can one construct a prime number consisting of 65 decimal digits? Are there other ways to solve equation (2)? In fact, if we can solve (2) sufficiently quickly without computing the secret exponent d or without factoring the number m, then the RSA cryptosystem will be broken. Surely, the reader can think about other questions as well.

Let us start from the end. Nobody managed to decrypt the phrase suggested in [56] for long 17 years before [4] appeared. Of course, this is only an indirect confirmation of the high security level of the RSA cryptosystem, but a rather convincing one. Below we discuss theoretical problems arising in solving polynomial congruences.

We are not going to discuss processing of large integers; the reader is referred to the remarkable book [43, Chapter 4] by D. Knuth. We only note that it is always possible to split a large integer into smaller blocks, and a computer can process these blocks in the way we usually operate with decimal digits when making calculations on a sheet of paper. Of course, these manipulations require special software. Even some special programming languages, PARI and UBASIC among them, were implemented for this purpose. These programming languages are free. The book [18] contains the information about how to implement them.

3. Complexity of number-theoretic algorithms

The usual measure of complexity of number-theoretic algorithms is the number of arithmetic operations (additions, subtractions, multiplications, and integer divisions) required to execute all steps of the algorithm. This definition, however, does not take into account the length of the numbers involved in the computations. Obviously, multiplication of two 100-digit numbers is much more complicated than that of 1-digit ones, although both are viewed as a single operation. This is why sometimes the complexity is measured in so-called bit operations, that is, operations with the binary digits 0 and 1 of the binary representations of numbers being processed. The precise definition usually depends on the problem under consideration, on author's goals, and so on.

It also seems unnatural to assign the same complexity to the multiplication/division and to the addition/subtraction operations. The common sense says that multiplying numbers requires more effort than adding them. However, there are multiplication algorithms with the number of bit operations close to that required for addition. In [2] the Schönhage–Strassen multiplication algorithm based on the so-called fast Fourier transform is described; this algorithm requires $O(n \log n \log \log n)$ bit operations for multiplication of two n-bit numbers. The same number of bit operations suffices for the integer division of two n-bit binary numbers. For comparison, we note that the sum of two n-bit binary numbers can be found in $O(n)$ bit operations.

Below, when discussing the complexity of algorithms, we mean the number of arithmetic operations. The intuition in the area of mathematics from which the algorithm came is usually sufficient for constructing efficient algorithms and upper estimates of their complexity. Formal definitions are required only if we prove lower bounds for complexity. For a more detailed and formal discussion, see Chapter 2.

Now let us give some examples of sufficiently efficient algorithms and estimate there complexity. Here we give only informal descriptions of the algorithms and try to explain the heart of the matter.

The following algorithm computes $a^d \bmod m$ in $O(\log d)$ arithmetic operations. We assume, of course, that both numbers a and d are not greater than m.

1. The algorithm computing $a^d \bmod m$.

1. Represent d in binary notation, $d = d_0 2^r + \cdots + d_{r-1} 2 + d_r$, where each d_i is one of the binary digits 0 and 1, $d_0 = 1$.

2. Set $a_0 = a$ and compute, for $i = 1, \ldots, r$,

$$a_i \equiv a_{i-1}^2 \cdot a^{d_i} \bmod m.$$

3. The element a_r is the required residue $a^d \bmod m$.

The correctness of this algorithm follows from the identity

$$a_i \equiv a^{d_0 2^i + \cdots + d_i} \bmod m,$$

which can be easily proved by induction on i.

Since each iteration of Step 2 requires at most three multiplications modulo m, and this step is repeated $r \leq \log_2 d$ times, the complexity of the algorithm has an upper estimate $O(\log d)$.

The second example is the classical Euclid algorithm computing the greatest common divisor of two integers. We assume that two positive integers a and b are given and compute their greatest common divisor (a, b).

2. The Euclid algorithm.

1. Compute r, the residue of a modulo b, $a = bq + r$, $0 \leq r < b$.

2. If $r = 0$, then b is (a, b).

3. If $r \neq 0$, then substitute the pair $\langle b, r \rangle$ for the pair $\langle a, b \rangle$ and return to Step 1.

Omitting the proof that this algorithm indeed computes the greatest common divisor, we estimate its complexity.

Theorem 1. *The computation of the greatest common divisor* (a, b) *by means of the Euclid algorithm requires at most $5p$ divisions, where p is the number of digits in the decimal notation of the smallest of two numbers a and b.*

Proof. Set $r_0 = a > b$, and let $r_1, r_2, \ldots, r_n$ be the sequence of remainders occurring in the execution of the Euclid algorithm. Then

$$r_1 = b, \qquad 0 \leq r_{i+1} < r_i, \qquad i = 0, 1, \ldots, n - 1.$$

Set also $u_0 = 1$, $u_1 = 1$, $u_{k+1} = u_k + u_{k-1}$ for $k \geq 1$; this means that u_i is the Fibonacci sequence. By induction on i starting at $i = n - 1$ and descending to $i = 0$, it is easy to prove the inequality $r_{i+1} \geq u_{n-i}$, and since $u_n \geq 10^{(n-1)/5}$, the inequalities $10^p > b = r_1 \geq u_n \geq 10^{(n-1)/5}$ and $n < 5p + 1$ also hold. $\qquad \square$

A small modification of the Euclid algorithm allows one to solve rather quickly congruences of the form $ax \equiv 1 \bmod b$ under the condition $(a, b) = 1$. The last problem is equivalent to solving the equation $ax + by = 1$.

3. The algorithm for solving the equation $ax + by = 1$.

0. Initialize the matrix variable $E = \begin{pmatrix} 1 & 0 \\ 0 & 1 \end{pmatrix}$.

1. Compute the remainder r, $0 \leq r < b$, of the division of a by b, $a = bq + r$.

2. If $r = 0$, then the second column of the matrix E gives the vector $\begin{pmatrix} x \\ y \end{pmatrix}$ of solutions of the equation.

3. If $r \neq 0$, then substitute the matrix $E \cdot \begin{pmatrix} 0 & 1 \\ 1 & -q \end{pmatrix}$ for the matrix E.

4. Substitute the pair $\langle b, r \rangle$ for the pair $\langle a, b \rangle$ and return to Step 1.

If we denote by E_k the value of the matrix variable E before Step 2 after k divisions (Step 1), then, in the notation of the proof of Theorem 1, the equality $\langle a, b \rangle \cdot E_k = \langle r_{k-1}, r_k \rangle$ holds. It can easily be proved by induction on k. Since the numbers a and b are relatively prime, we have $r_n = 1$, and this confirms that the algorithm indeed solves the equation $ax + by = 1$. We denote by n the number of divisions, which coincides with that in the Euclid algorithm.

The three algorithms above are polynomial time. This class consists of algorithms whose complexity has a polynomial upper bound in the length of input numbers (see details in Chapter 2). If the largest of the input numbers of the algorithm is not greater than m, then the complexity of algorithms of this kind is $O((\log m)^c)$, where c is an absolute constant for the given algorithm. In all examples above $c = 1$.

Polynomial time algorithms are very rare in number theory. Moreover, even the majority of known estimates is based on some yet unproved but plausible conjectures from analytic number theory.

For some problems no efficient algorithm is known. In some cases it is possible, however, to suggest a sequence of operations which leads, if we are lucky, to a "successful" result. There is a class of so-called probabilistic algorithms that lead to a correct result, but the estimates of their working time are of probabilistic nature. Usually the working time of these algorithms depends on some parameters. In the worst case, they work for a rather long time, but a convenient choice of the parameters results in a quick execution. If the set of "convenient" parameter values is sufficiently large, then such algorithms are rather efficient in practice although there are no good complexity estimates.

Below, we shall sometimes use the adjective "deterministic" to distinguish usual algorithms from probabilistic ones.

As an example, consider the probabilistic algorithm that allows one to solve efficiently polynomial congruences modulo a prime number. Let p be a prime integer, which is supposed to be large, and let $f(x) \in \mathbb{Z}[x]$ be a polynomial of bounded degree. The problem consists in solving the polynomial congruence

$$(8) \qquad\qquad f(x) \equiv 0 \bmod p.$$

For example, if the degree of f is 2, then we study quadratic congruences. In other words, we want to find all elements of the field $F_p = \mathbb{Z}/p\mathbb{Z}$ satisfying the equation $f(x) = 0$.

According to Fermat's Little Theorem, all elements of the field $\mathbb{F}_p$ are roots of multiplicity one of the polynomial $x^p - x$. Therefore, the polynomial $d(x)$, whose roots in $\mathbb{F}_p$ coincide with those of $f(x)$ and all roots have multiplicity one, is the greatest common divisor $d(x) = (x^p - x, f(x))$. If the degree of $d(x)$ happens to be zero, that is, $d(x)$ is a nonzero element of $\mathbb{F}_p$, then congruence (8) has no solutions.

It is convenient to start the computation of the polynomial $d(x)$ with calculating the polynomial $c(x) \equiv x^p \bmod f(x)$ using an algorithm similar to the above algorithm for computing powers (recall that p is assumed to be large). Then the polynomial $d(x) = (c(x) - x, f(x))$ can be computed by the Euclid algorithm. All these calculations can be performed in a polynomial number of arithmetic operations.

Therefore, in discussing how to solve congruence (8) we can assume that the equation

$$f(x) = (x - a_1) \cdots (x - a_n), \qquad a_i \in \mathbb{F}_p, a_i \neq a_j,$$

holds in the ring of polynomials $\mathbb{F}_p[x]$.

4. The algorithm for computing the divisors of a polynomial $f(x)$ in the ring $\mathbb{F}_p[x]$.

1. Choose a random element $\delta \in \mathbb{F}_p$.

2. Compute the greatest common divisor

$$g(x) = (f(x), (x + \delta)^{\frac{p-1}{2}} - 1).$$

3. If the polynomial $g(x)$ is a proper divisor of $f(x)$, then we obtain a factorization of $f(x)$ into a product of two polynomials, and we must apply the algorithm to each factor.

4. If either $g(x) = 1$, or $g(x) = f(x)$, then return to Step 1 and repeat the algorithm for a different value of δ.

Step 2, if done in the same way as the computation of $d(x)$ above, requires $O(\log p)$ operations. Now let us count the number of choices of δ before we find a proper factor of $f(x)$ in Step 2.

The number of solutions of the equation $(t+a_1)^{\frac{p-1}{2}} = (t+a_2)^{\frac{p-1}{2}}$ in the field $\mathbb{F}_p$ is not greater than $\frac{p-3}{2}$. This means that the subset $D \subset \mathbb{F}_q$ consisting of elements δ such that

$$(\delta + a_1)^{\frac{p-1}{2}} \neq (\delta + a_2)^{\frac{p-1}{2}}, \qquad \delta \neq -a_1, \quad \delta \neq -a_2,$$

contains at least $\frac{p-1}{2}$ elements. Taking into account that for each nonzero element $b \in \mathbb{F}_p$ we have either $b^{\frac{p-1}{2}} = 1$, or $b^{\frac{p-1}{2}} = -1$, we conclude that for $\delta \in D$ one of the numbers a_1, a_2 is a root of the polynomial $(x + \delta)^{\frac{p-1}{2}} - 1$, while the other is not. For such elements δ the polynomial $g(x)$ introduced in Step 2 is a proper divisor of the polynomial $f(x)$.

This means that there are at least $\frac{p-1}{2}$ "lucky" choices of δ that lead to a splitting of the polynomial $f(x)$ into a product of two proper divisors in Step 2. Therefore, under a "random" choice of an element $\delta \in \mathbb{F}_p$ the probability that the polynomial will not split into a product of proper factors after k iterations of Steps 1–4 is not greater than 2^{-k}. It decreases very rapidly as k grows. In practice this algorithm works rather efficiently.

Note that when estimating the probability we used only two roots of the polynomial $f(x)$. For $n > 2$ this probability is, of course, even lower. A more delicate analysis using Weil's estimates for trigonometric sums shows that the probability for a polynomial $f(x)$ not split into a product after a single iteration of the algorithm is not greater than $2^{-n} + O(p^{-1/2})$. Here the normalizing constant in $O(\cdot)$ depends on n; see details in [8]. For an elementary proof of Weil's estimate, see [62].

In the book [43] a deterministic algorithm of solving congruence (8) introduced by Berlekamp is described. This algorithm requires $O(pn^3)$ arithmetic operations. It is useless for large p, but for small p and not too large n it works rather quickly.

If the prime module p in congruence (8) is replaced with a composite module m, then the solution problem for the new congruence becomes much more difficult. The known algorithms of solving it are based on a reduction of the congruence to a system of congruences (8) with prime moduli that are divisors of m; therefore, they require the decomposition of m into prime factors, which is, as we know already, a rather complicated problem.

4. How to distinguish between a composite and a prime number

There is a rather efficient way to understand whether a given number is composite without decomposing it into a product. By Fermat's Little Theorem, if N is a prime number, then the congruence

$$(9) \qquad\qquad a^{N-1} \equiv 1 \qquad \mod N$$

holds for arbitrary integer a not divisible by N. If this congruence fails for some a not divisible by N, then we conclude that N is composite. The only problem consists in finding, for a given composite number N, an integer a that does not satisfy (9). For example, we can try all integers starting with 2, or take a random number in the interval $1 < a < N$.

Unfortunately, this approach is not always efficient. There are integers N possessing property (9) for all numbers a satisfying the condition $(a, N) = 1$. Such numbers are called Carmichael numbers. Take, for example, the number $561 = 3 \cdot 11 \cdot 17$. Since 560 is divisible by each of the numbers $2, 10, 16$, Fermat's Little Theorem easily implies that 561 is a Carmichael number. One can prove (Carmichael, 1912) that each Carmichael number N has the form $N = p_1 \cdots p_r$, $r \geq 3$, where p_i are pairwise distinct prime numbers, and $N-1$ is divisible by each of the numbers $p_i - 1$. The infiniteness of the set of Carmichael numbers was proved only recently; see [**3**].

In 1976 Miller suggested to replace condition (9) with a different one. Details of the discussion below can be found in [**65**]. If N is a prime number, and $N - 1 = 2^s \cdot t$, where t is odd, then by Fermat's Little Theorem, for each a such that $(a, N) = 1$, at least one of the factors in the product

$$(a^t - 1)(a^t + 1)(a^{2t} + 1) \cdots (a^{2^{s-1}} + 1) = a^{N-1} - 1$$

is divisible by N. Inverting this property we obtain a test for distinguishing between composite and prime numbers.

Let N be an odd composite number, $N - 1 = 2^s \cdot t$, where t is odd. We call a number a, $1 < a < N$, "*good*" for N if at least one of the following two conditions is violated:

α) N is not divisible by a;

β) either $a^t \equiv 1 \mod N$, or there is an integer k, $0 \le k < s$, such that

$$a^{2^k t} \equiv -1 \mod N.$$

The discussion above implies that there are no good numbers for a prime number N. On the contrary, if N is composite, then as was proved by Rabin, there are at least $\frac{3}{4}(N-1)$ good numbers for it. Now we can suggest a probabilistic algorithm that distinguishes composite numbers from prime ones.

5. The algorithm that proves that a given number is composite.

1. Choose randomly a number a, $1 < a < N$, and verify conditions α) and β) above for this number.

2. If at least one of the conditions fails, then N is composite.

3. If both conditions α) and β) are satisfied, then return to Step 1.

It follows from the discussion above that the probability of not identifying a composite number after a single iteration is at most 4^{-1}. And after k iterations, this probability is not greater than 4^{-k}, i.e., it decreases very rapidly.

Miller suggested also a deterministic algorithm with complexity $O(\log^3 N)$ for distinguishing composite numbers. However, the correctness of his algorithm follows from the generalized Riemann hypothesis, which remains unproved so far. According to his algorithm, it suffices to verify conditions α) and β) for all integers a in the interval $2 \le a \le 70 \log^2 N$. If one of the conditions fails for some number from this interval, then N is composite. Otherwise it is either prime, or a power of a prime number. A verification of the last possibility is easy.

Now we are going to formulate the generalized Riemann hypothesis, and we start with recalling some required notions; see [41]. They will also be useful later. Let $m \geq 2$ be an integer. A function $\chi : \mathbb{Z} \to \mathbb{C}$ is called a *Dirichlet character* modulo m, or simply a *character*, if it is periodic with period m, takes nonzero values only on numbers prime to m, and is multiplicative, i.e., for arbitrary integers u, v the equality $\chi(uv) = \chi(u)\chi(v)$ holds. There are precisely $\varphi(m)$ Dirichlet characters for each m. They form a group with respect to the multiplication of characters. The unit element of this group is the so-called principal character χ_0, which takes value 1 on all numbers prime to m, and value 0 otherwise. The *order* of a character is the order of the corresponding element of the multiplicative group of characters.

To a character χ we associate the so-called *Dirichlet L-function*, which is a function of a complex variable s defined by the series $L(s, \chi) = \sum_{n=1}^{\infty} \frac{\chi(n)}{n^s}$. The sum of this series is analytic in the domain Re $s > 1$, and it can be extended analytically to the entire complex plane. The L-function corresponding to the principal character is related to the Riemann ζ-function $\zeta(s) = \prod_{n=0}^{\infty} \frac{1}{n^s}$ by the formula $L(s, \chi_0) = \zeta(s) \prod_{p|m}(1 - p^{-s})$. The generalized Riemann hypothesis states that the complex zeroes of all Dirichlet L-functions, all of which are situated in the domain $0 < $ Re $s < 1$, lie on the line Re $s = \frac{1}{2}$. Presently, even the simplest version of this conjecture concerning the zeroes of the Riemann ζ-function remains open.

In 1952 Ankeney proved, using the generalized Riemann hypothesis, that for each prime number q there is a quadratic nonresidue a in the interval $2 \leq a \leq 70 \log^2 q$ (the constant 70 was computed later). This statement forms the base of Miller's result. In 1957 Burgess proved the existence of such a nonresidue without using the generalized Riemann hypothesis, but with a worse estimate $2 \leq a \leq q^{\frac{1}{4\sqrt{e}}+\varepsilon}$, which is true for arbitrary positive ε and for q exceeding some upper bound depending on ε.

In contrast to Algorithm 5, Miller's algorithm may turn out to be false since it is based on the generalized Riemann hypothesis, which has not been proved yet. In spite of lack of precise estimates, in practice, Algorithm 5 is sufficiently efficient.

5. How to construct large prime numbers

We are not going to discuss the history of the problem here, and we refer the reader to the book [**43**] and to the surveys [**65, 62**]. Of course, there are efficient algorithms for constructing large prime numbers, and the prime numbers thus constructed are distributed randomly in a given range. Otherwise, the RSA cryptosystem would be useless. The most efficient way of constructing prime numbers is a slightly modified Fermat's Little Theorem.

Theorem 2. *Let N and S be odd integers such that $N - 1 = S \cdot R$ for some integer R, and suppose that for each prime factor q of S there is an integer a such that*

$$(10) \qquad a^{N-1} \equiv 1 \mod N \ \text{and} \ (a^{\frac{N-1}{q}} - 1, N) = 1.$$

Then each prime divisor p of N satisfies the congruence

$$p \equiv 1 \bmod 2S.$$

Proof. Let p be a prime divisor of N, and let q be a divisor of S. Assumptions (10) imply that

$$(11) \qquad a^{N-1} = 1, \quad a^{\frac{N-1}{q}} \neq 1, \quad a^{p-1} = 1$$

in the residue field $\mathbb{F}_p$. Denote by r the order of a in the multiplicative group of $\mathbb{F}_p$. The first two relations in (11) mean that the degree of q in the decomposition of r into prime factors coincides with the degree of q in the decomposition of $N - 1$ into prime factors, and the last relation implies that $p - 1$ is divisible by r. Thus, the degree of each prime factor in the decomposition of S is not less than its degree in the decomposition of $p - 1$, whence $p - 1$ is divisible by S. Besides, $p - 1$ is even. Theorem 2 is proved. $\qquad \square$

Corollary. *Under the assumptions of Theorem 2, if $R \leq 4S + 2$, then N is prime.*

Indeed, suppose N is a product of at least two prime numbers. By Theorem 2, each of the factors is at least $2S + 1$. Then $(2S+1)^2 \leq N = SR + 1 \leq 4S^2 + 2S + 1$. This contradiction proves the corollary.

Now let us show how, using this corollary, one can find a large prime number N starting from a much smaller prime number S. Let us choose randomly an even number R in the interval $S \le R \le 4S+2$ and set $N = SR + 1$. Then we check whether N has small prime divisors by dividing it by small prime numbers, and apply Algorithm 5 to N several times. If it happens that N is a composite number, then we choose the new value of R and repeat all computations. This procedure is repeated until we find a number N that passes a sufficient number of iterations of Algorithm 5. In this case we can hope that N is prime, and we can try to prove the primality using the criteria of Theorem 2.

In order to do this, we can choose randomly a number a in the interval $1 < a < N$ and verify that the equations

$$(12) \qquad a^{N-1} \equiv 1 \mod N, \qquad (a^R - 1, N) = 1$$

hold. If these equations are satisfied, then, by Corollary from Theorem 2, N is prime. Otherwise we must choose another value of a and repeat the procedure until we find a required test number a.

Suppose the number N thus constructed is indeed prime. Let us estimate how many times we should choose a number a until we find the number satisfying conditions (12). Note that, by Fermat's Little Theorem, for a prime N the first equation in (12) always holds. The numbers a violating the second equation in (12) are subject to the congruence $a^R \equiv 1 \mod N$. It is well known that the last congruence has at most R solutions in the field $\mathbb{F}_N$. One of these solutions is $x = 1$. Therefore, there are at most $R - 1$ elements in the interval $1 < a < N$ not satisfying (12). This means that for N prime, a random choice of a from the interval $1 < a < N$ produces a number a satisfying the assumptions of Theorem 2, and thus proves that N indeed is prime with probability greater than $1 - O(S^{-1})$.

Note that the prime number N constructed in this way satisfies the condition $N > S^2$, i.e., it requires two times more digits to be written down than the initial prime number S. Now, replacing S with the newly generated prime number N and repeating all the constructions above starting with the new value of S we can construct an even larger prime number. If we start with a small prime number (say, containing ten digits in the decimal notation) whose primality can be verified directly by dividing over table prime numbers, and iterate the process a sufficient number of times, then we can construct prime numbers of required length.

Now let us discuss some theoretical questions arising in connection with the search for prime numbers of the form $N = SR+1$, where the numbers R and S satisfy the inequalities $S \leq R \leq 4S+2$. First of all, by the Dirichlet theorem proved already in 1839, the progression $2Sn + 1$, $n = 1, 2, 3, \ldots$, contains an infinite set of prime numbers. We are interested in prime numbers that are not too far from the beginning of the progression. In 1944 Yu. V. Linnik gave an estimate for the smallest prime number in such progression. Linnik's estimate states that the smallest prime number in a progression $2Sn + 1$ does not exceed S^C, where C is a (rather big) absolute constant. Assuming the Riemann conjecture to be true, we can produce an upper bound for the smallest prime element in the form $c(\varepsilon) \cdot S^{2+\varepsilon}$ for an arbitrarily small positive ε.

Thus, up to now there is no theoretical justification of the existence of a prime number of the form $N = SR+1$ for $S \leq R \leq 4S+2$. Nevertheless, computer calculations show that usually there are prime numbers in arithmetic progressions that are rather close to the beginning. We must also mention the conjecture stating that the set of prime numbers q such that $2q + 1$ is also prime (i.e., already the first term of the progression is prime) is infinite.

In connection with the approach to constructing prime numbers described above, the following question is also important: what is the distance between neighboring prime numbers in a progression? Indeed, after verifying that a number $N = SR + 1$ is composite, we can replace R with $R + 2$ and proceed in this way until we find a prime number N. If the distance between neighboring prime numbers is large, then there is no hope that we will construct a prime number N in a short time. The exhaustive search for the required number R can be too long. The distance between two consecutive prime numbers p_n and p_{n+1} in the simplest situation of all positive integers is only known to be $p_{n+1} - p_n = O(p_n^{\frac{38}{61}+\varepsilon})$, which is not sufficient for our purposes. On the other hand, the so-called Cramer's conjecture (1936) says that $p_{n+1} - p_n = O(\log^2 p_n)$, and this estimate is much better. Approximately the same estimate follows from the generalized Riemann hypothesis. Computer experiments show that prime elements are rather dense in arithmetic progressions.

We complete the discussion in the present section by emphasizing the following fact. If we believe that the smallest prime number as well as the distance between consecutive prime numbers in an arithmetic progression $2Sn + 1$ for $S \leq n \leq 4S + 2$ are of order $O(\log^2 S)$, then the scheme for constructing large prime numbers described above has a polynomial complexity. Besides, in spite of lack of good theoretical estimates for the time of finding prime elements in progressions with rather large differences, in practice these algorithms are sufficiently good. A prime number of order 10^{300} can be constructed in this way on a usual personal computer in a reasonable time.

Of course, the method of constructing prime numbers for an RSA algorithm implementation must be a general one, and the constructed prime numbers must be well distributed in some sense, which causes additional difficulties. However, the scheme above admits a number of modifications. The related problems are discussed in details in [**52**].

Finally, let us note that there are ways to produce large prime numbers using not only the prime factors of $N - 1$, but also the divisors of $N + 1$, $N^2 + 1$, $N^2 \pm N + 1$. These methods exploit properties of integer sequences satisfying linear recurrence relations of various orders. Note that the sequence a^n, which enters the statement of Fermat's Little Theorem, is the solution to the linear recurrence relation of order one: $u_{n+1} = au_n$, $u_0 = 1$.

6. How to test primality of a large number

The problem we are going to address in this section differs slightly from the problem in the previous one. When constructing a large prime number N, we possess some additional information about it. For example, we know the prime divisors of $N - 1$. Sometimes, this additional information allows us to simplify the primality proof.

In contrast, in this section we assume that a positive integer N is given, say, by a random selection from some interval, and we must either prove that it is prime, or show that it is composite. Miller's algorithm from Section 4 solves this problem in polynomial time. However, this algorithm is provably correct only under the assumption that the generalized Riemann hypothesis is true. Another approach consists in using Algorithm 5. If a number N passed 100 tests with different values of a, then we can claim that N is prime with probability greater than $1 - 4^{-100}$. This probability is very close to 1, but there still remains a shadow of doubt. Below in this section we assume that N is a prime number, and we only need to prove this.

Currently, we know several deterministic algorithms of different complexity for proving that a number is prime. We discuss in more detail the algorithm suggested by Adleman, Pomerance, and Rumeli in [1]. The primality proof using this algorithm requires $(\log N)^{c \log \log \log N}$ arithmetic operations. Here c is some absolute positive constant. The function $\log \log \log N$ grows slowly as N grows, so that the algorithm is in fact not polynomial. However, in practice it gives sufficiently quick primality tests. The initial version of the algorithm was improved and simplified soon afterwards in the papers by Lenstra and Cohen [45, 19]. We call the algorithm presented below the Adleman–Lenstra algorithm.

The algorithm is based on congruences similar to those used in Fermat's Little Theorem, but valid in rings of integers of cyclotomic fields, that is, fields generated over $\mathbb{Q}$ by roots of unity $\zeta_p = e^{2\pi i/p}$. Let q be an odd prime integer, and let c be a primitive root of unity modulo q, that is, a generator of the (cyclic) multiplicative group of the field $\mathbb{F}_q$. For each integer x not divisible by q the congruence $x \equiv c^{\operatorname{ind}_q x} \bmod q$ defines the *index* $\operatorname{ind}_q x \in \mathbb{Z}/(q-1)\mathbb{Z}$ of x, also called the *discrete logarithm*. Let p, q be two prime integers such that $q - 1$ is divisible by p, but not by p^2.

The function

$$\chi(x) = \begin{cases} 0 & \text{if } q|x, \\ \zeta_p^{\operatorname{ind}_q x} & \text{if } (x, q) = 1, \end{cases}$$

defined on integers, is a character modulo q, and the order of this character is p. The sum

$$\tau(\chi) = -\sum_{x=1}^{q-1} \chi(x)\zeta_q^x \in \mathbb{Z}[\zeta_p, \zeta_q]$$

is called the *Gauss sum*. Theorem 3 below is an analogue of Fermat's Little Theorem used in the Adleman–Lenstra algorithm.

Theorem 3. *Let N be an odd prime number such that $(N, pq) = 1$. Then the congruence*

$$\tau(\chi)^N \equiv \chi(N)^{-N} \cdot \tau(\chi^N) \bmod N\mathbb{Z}[\zeta_p, \zeta_q]$$

holds in the ring $\mathbb{Z}[\zeta_p, \zeta_q]$.

If the congruence in Theorem 3 fails for some numbers p, q, then N is a composite number. Otherwise, if the congruence is true, then it produces some information about possible prime divisors of N. Gathering this information for various p and q we can conclude finally that N has only one prime factor and, therefore, is prime.

If $p = 2$, then it is easy to check that the congruence in Theorem 3 is equivalent to the congruence

$$(13) \qquad q^{\frac{N-1}{2}} \equiv \left(\frac{q}{N}\right) \bmod N,$$

which is well known in number theory. Here $\left(\frac{q}{N}\right)$ is the so-called *Jacobi symbol*. It is also well known that the latter congruence holds not only for prime q, but also for all q relatively prime to N. Note also that there is a fast algorithm for computing the Jacobi symbol based on the Gauss reciprocity law; this algorithm is, in a sense, similar to the Euclid algorithm of computing the greatest common divisor. The example below shows how to extract the information about possible prime divisors of N from the set of congruences (13).

Example 1 (H. Lenstra). Let N be an integer, $(N, 6) = 1$, such that

$$(14) \qquad a^{\frac{N-1}{2}} \equiv \left(\frac{a}{N}\right) \bmod N \text{ for } a = -1, 2, 3,$$

and, for some integer b,

$$(15) \qquad b^{\frac{N-1}{2}} \equiv -1 \bmod N.$$

As was mentioned above, if N is prime, then congruences (14) hold for an arbitrary a prime to N, and congruence (15) means that b is a quadratic nonresidue of N. The number of quadratic nonresidues is $\frac{N-1}{2}$, i.e., it is rather large. Thus, for a prime N, a number b satisfying (15) can be found sufficiently fast by a random choice and subsequent verification of (15).

Now let us prove that congruences (14)–(15) imply that each divisor r of N satisfies one of the congruences

(16) $r \equiv 1 \bmod 24$ or $r \equiv N \bmod 24$.

Without loss of generality we can assume that r is prime. Introduce the notation $N - 1 = u \cdot 2^k$, $r - 1 = v \cdot 2^m$, where both u and v are odd integers. Equation (15) and the congruence $b^{r-1} \equiv 1 \bmod r$ together imply that $m \geq k$. Now, by (14), the congruences

$$\left(\frac{a}{N}\right) = \left(\frac{a}{N}\right)^v \equiv a^{uv2^{k-1}} \bmod r, \qquad \left(\frac{a}{r}\right) = \left(\frac{a}{r}\right)^u \equiv a^{uv2^{m-1}} \bmod r$$

hold; this means (since the Jacobi symbol takes only values -1 and $+1$) that

$$\left(\frac{a}{N}\right)^{2^{m-k}} = \left(\frac{a}{r}\right).$$

If $m > k$, then the last equation means that $\left(\frac{a}{r}\right) = 1$ for $a = -1, 2, 3$, and, therefore, $r \equiv 1 \bmod 24$. And if $m = k$, then we have $\left(\frac{a}{N}\right) = \left(\frac{a}{r}\right)$, and $r \equiv N \bmod 24$, which proves (16).

Similar information can be extracted in the case of arbitrary prime numbers p and q possessing the above properties.

Let us describe (briefly) the Adleman–Lenstra algorithm for the verification of primality of N:

1) choose pairwise distinct prime numbers $p_1, \dots, p_k$ and pairwise distinct odd prime numbers $q_1, \dots, q_s$ such that

a) for each j all prime divisors of $q_j - 1$ are among the numbers $p_1, \dots, p_k$, and the number $q_j - 1$ is not divisible by the square of a prime number,

b) $S = 2q_1 \cdots q_s > \sqrt{N}$;

2) a test similar to the congruence in Theorem 3 is executed for each chosen pair p, q. If N does not satisfy one of the tests, then it is composite. Otherwise,

3) a small set of numbers is chosen in such a way that each prime divisor of N is congruent modulo N to one of these numbers. Namely, each prime divisor of N must satisfy a congruence of the form

$$r \equiv N^j \quad \bmod S, \quad 0 \leq j < T = p_1 \cdots p_k;$$

4) check whether this set contains a divisor of N. If there are no divisors in it, then N is a prime number.

If the number N is composite, then it necessarily has a prime divisor r less than $\sqrt{N} < S$ that belongs to the set of possible remainders itself. This property is the base of Step 4 of the algorithm.

Example 2. The sets

$$p \in \{2, 3, 5, 7\} \text{ and } q \in \{3, 7, 11, 31, 43, 71, 211\}$$

allow one to check the primality of all numbers $N < 8.5 \cdot 10^{19}$.

Note that in [1] not the congruences of Theorem 3 but the reciprocity law for power residues and so-called Jacobi sums were used for testing. The *Jacobi sum*

$$J(\chi_1, \chi_2) = -\sum_{x=2}^{q-1} \chi_1(x)\chi_2(1-x)$$

is defined for two characters χ_1, χ_2 modulo q. If both characters are of order p, then the corresponding Jacobi sum belongs to the ring $\mathbb{Z}[\zeta_p]$. Since the numbers p from the algorithm are relatively small, the calculations with Jacobi sums are executed in fields of degree much less than the degree required for computations of Gauss sums. This is the main reason why Jacobi sums are more convenient. If $\chi_1\chi_2 \neq \chi_0$, then the classical equality

$$J(\chi_1, \chi_2) = \frac{\tau(\chi_1) \cdot \tau(\chi_2)}{\tau(\chi_1 \cdot \chi_2)}$$

relating Gauss sums to Jacobi sums holds. This equality allows one to rewrite the congruence in Theorem 3 in terms of Jacobi sums (see [55]). For example, for $p = 3$ and $q = 7$ the corresponding congruence valid for all prime N except $2, 3, 7$ is

$$(-3\zeta - 2)^{\left[\frac{N}{3}\right]} \cdot (3\zeta + 1)^{\left[\frac{2N}{3}\right]} \equiv \xi \mod (N, \mathbb{Z}[\zeta]),$$

where $\zeta = e^{2\pi i/3}$ and ξ is a cubic root of 1.

In [19] an essential improvement was suggested allowing the algorithm to get rid of the requirement that $q - 1$ admits no squares of prime numbers as divisors. As a result, taking $T = 2^4 \cdot 3^2 \cdot 5 \cdot 7 = 5040$ and choosing S equal to the product of all prime numbers q such that

T is divisible by $q-1$ we obtain $S > 1.5 \cdot 10^{52}$, and this allows one to prove primality of numbers N having hundred digits in the decimal notation. The computations are to be done in fields generated by roots of unity of degree $16, 9, 5,$ and 7.

It took 8 seconds for the implementation of this algorithm in UBASIC on our personal computer with Pentium-150 processor to prove the primality of the largest of the two prime numbers from the example of Rivest, Shamir, and Adleman having 65 digits in the decimal notation (see Section 1). A notable achievement when compared to 17 years required for the factorization of the number from the example!

Note that the upper estimate $(\log N)^{c \log \log \log N}$ for the number of operations in this algorithm mentioned above is a result of complicated arguments from analytical number theory. The numbers S and T arising in the proof cannot be described explicitly in terms of N. Only the existence of the numbers that guarantee the estimate is proved. Besides, there is a probabilistic version of the algorithm, which proves, provided that the generalized Riemann hypothesis is true, the primality of a prime number N with probability greater than $1 - 2^{-k}$ in $O(k(\log N)^{c \log \log \log N})$ arithmetic operations, and for this version the numbers S and T can be chosen explicitly.

A polynomial algorithm for testing primality of a large number N was recently proposed by M. Agraval, N. Kayal, and N. Saxena. The complexity of this algorithm is $O(\log^{12} N)$.

7. How to factorize a composite number

We will briefly discuss the topic mentioned in the title of this section. For further reading, we recommend the books [**43, 55, 18**].[2] Among the variety of factorization algorithms we have chosen one that yields the factorization of the number m in the RSA sample.

People were looking for efficient ways to factorize integers for a long time. Prominent specialists in number theory paid serious attention to this problem. Probably Fermat was the first who tried to present a number N as the difference of two squares, $N = x^2 - y^2$, and

---

[2]See also [**68**]. (*Added in translation.*)

then to look for a nontrivial divisor of N by computing $(N, x - y)$. He also suggested a way to find the required presentation. If the number to be factorized has two divisors with a rather small difference, then this way is more efficient than the exhaustive search of divisors. Legendre noticed that it suffices to get the congruence

$$(17) \qquad\qquad x^2 \equiv y^2 \bmod N.$$

Of course, not every solution of this congruence allows one to factorize N. Both Euler and Gauss suggested some ways to find solutions of (17). Legendre used *continued fractions*.

Recall that with each irrational number ξ one can associate an infinite sequence of integers $[b_0; b_1, b_2, \dots]$, which is called the continued fraction of ξ. The construction proceeds as follows. We set[3]

$$x_0 = \xi, \quad b_i = [x_i], \quad x_{i+1} = \frac{1}{x_i - b_i}, \quad i = 0, 1, 2, \dots .$$

Legendre proved that the continued fraction of a quadratic irrationality is periodic. If we start with $\xi = \sqrt{N}$, then all the numbers x_i arising in the decomposition process are of the form $x_i = \frac{\sqrt{N} + P_i}{Q_i}$ with integers P_i and Q_i such that $0 \leq P_i \leq \sqrt{N}$ and $0 \leq Q_i \leq 2\sqrt{N}$. To a continued fraction, a sequence of rational numbers $\frac{A_i}{B_i}$, $i \geq 0$, the so-called convergents, is associated. Here

$$A_{i+1} = b_{i+1}A_i + A_{i-1}, \quad B_{i+1} = b_{i+1}B_i + B_{i-1}, \quad i \geq 0,$$
$$A_0 = b_0, \quad B_0 = A_{-1} = 1, \quad B_{-1} = 0,$$

and the convergents tend to the expanded number. If the number is $\xi = \sqrt{N}$, then the relation

$$(18) \qquad\qquad A_{i-1}^2 - NB_{i-1}^2 = (-1)^i Q_i$$

holds. The last equation implies the congruence

$$(19) \qquad\qquad A_{i-1}^2 \equiv (-1)^i Q_i \bmod N.$$

Note that the length of the period in the continued fraction for a quadratic irrationality $\xi = \sqrt{N}$ can be as large as $\sqrt{N}$.

In 1971 Schanks suggested the use of congruences (19) for constructing numbers satisfying (17). Repeating the calculation of the

---

[3]$[x]$ denotes the integer part of x.

continued fraction until $Q_i = R^2$ is obtained for some even i and integer R, we get a pair of numbers $\langle A_{i-1}, R \rangle$ satisfying condition (17), and we may hope to obtain a factorization of N by means of this pair.

In 1975 Morrison and Brillhart suggested that congruences (19) for different values of i be multiplied, trying to obtain in this way the square of an integer on the right-hand side. This continued fraction method produced the first factorization of the seventh Fermat number $F_7 = 2^{128} + 1$. The algorithm starts with the so-called base of factors $\{p_1, p_2, \ldots, p_s\}$. It contains prime numbers bounded by some value and such that $\left(\frac{N}{p_i} \right) = 1$. The last condition is imposed because, by (18), only those primes for which N is a quadratic residue can be divisors of Q_i.

On the first stage, each number Q_i is divided by all the numbers $p_1, p_2, \ldots, p_s$, and if it cannot be presented as a product of powers of these prime factors, then it is rejected. Otherwise we obtain a decomposition

$$(20) \qquad (-1)^i Q_i = (-1)^{a_0} \prod_{j=1}^{s} p_j^{a_j}.$$

Next we associate to this number i the vector $(a_0, a_1, \ldots, a_s)$, that is, the vector of exponents, and compute the next value Q_{i+1}, and the entire procedure is repeated.

These calculations are iterated until $s + 2$ vectors of exponents are constructed. Obviously, it is possible to choose a set of rows in the resulting matrix of exponents in such a way that their sum be a vector with even coordinates $2(b_0, b_1, \ldots, b_s)$. Denote this set by Δ. Then it is easy to check, using (19), that the congruence

$$\left(\prod_{i \in \Delta} A_{i-1} \right)^2 \equiv \left(\prod_{j=1}^{s} p_j^{b_j} \right)^2 \bmod N$$

holds.

If the last congruence does not allow us to factorize N, then the procedure is repeated.

The algorithm sketched above was improved as follows. The continued fraction for the number $\sqrt{kN}$ can be substituted for that for $\sqrt{N}$, and we can choose the factor k in such a way that all small primes enter the base of factors; the so-called early interruption strategy was suggested, and so on. The upper estimate

$$O(\exp(\sqrt{1.5 \cdot \log N \cdot \log \log N}))$$

for the complexity of this algorithm was obtained in 1982 under some reliable but yet unproved assumptions about the distribution of prime numbers. The function in the estimate grows more slowly than an arbitrary exponent. Algorithms of complexity admitting an estimate satisfying this property are called subexponential (with respect to $\log N$).

In 1982 Pomerance proposed a new quadratic sieve algorithm, which is also subexponential. The complexity of this algorithm admits an upper bound similar to that in the continued fraction method, but with the constant $9/8$ instead of 1.5. Let $m = \left[\sqrt{N}\right]$, $Q(x) = (x+m)^2 - N$, and choose the same base of factors as in the continued fraction method. For small values of x the value $Q(x)$ is also relatively small. The next step explains the name of the method. Instead of searching through all numbers x and factorizing all respective values $Q(x)$, the algorithm starts with rejecting all x except those for which there is an element dividing $Q(x)$ in the base of factors.

Specifying a bound B we find, for each prime p in the base of factors and each exponent a such that $p^a \leq B$, the solutions x of the quadratic congruence $Q(x) \equiv 0 \bmod p^a$. Denote the set of solutions by Λ. For each $x \in \Lambda$ there is at least one element in the base of factors some power of which occurs in the decomposition of $Q(x)$ into prime factors. The value x such that $Q(x)$ happens to be totally factorized gives a vector of exponents similar to that in the continued fractions algorithm. If there are sufficiently many such vectors, then the operations of the continued fraction algorithm can be applied.

We described briefly only the main idea of the algorithm. In addition to it, a number of other arguments and tricks are applied. For example, the congruence

$$(21) \qquad Q(x) \equiv q_1 q_2 (-1)^{a_0} \prod_{j=1}^{s} p_j^{a_j} \bmod N$$

serves as an analogue of (20). Here q_1, q_2 are two additional large prime numbers, $B_1 < q_i < B_2$. They are eliminated later as the values $Q(x)$ are multiplied.

The reader can find some details of the algorithm implementation in [43]. Here we only remark that the factorization procedure was applied to the number $5N$, and the base of factors contained -1 as well as 524338 prime numbers less than $B_1 = 16333609$. The additional bound was $B_2 = 2^{30}$. The result of sifting consisted of 112011 congruences of the form (21) without factors q_i, 1431337 congruences with one such factor, and 6881138 congruences with two factors. It was the search for these congruences that took 220 days and a large number of computers working in parallel. The construction of even vectors of exponents from congruences (21) on the second stage required working with matrices of size hundreds of thousands of bits. This second stage took 45 hours. The fourth vector with even exponents gave the required factorization.

8. Discrete logarithms

Let p be an odd prime number. It was known already to Euler that the multiplicative group of the ring $\mathbb{Z}/p\mathbb{Z}$ is cyclic, i.e., there is an integer a such that the congruence

$$(22) \qquad\qquad a^x \equiv b \bmod p$$

has a solution x for arbitrary $b \in \mathbb{Z}$ not divisible by p. Such numbers a are called primitive roots, and there are $\varphi(p) - 1$ of them, where φ is the Euler function. The solution x of (22) is called the index, or the discrete logarithm of b.

In Section 2 we described an algorithm allowing one to compute, for a given x, the value $a^x \bmod p$ sufficiently quickly. However, the computation of the inverse function, the discrete logarithm of a given number b, is a complicated task from the computational point of view. It is precisely this property of the discrete logarithm that makes it widely applicable in cryptography (see Chapter 1). The fastest (known) algorithms of computing discrete logarithms require $\exp(c(\log p)^{1/3}(\log\log p)^{2/3})$ arithmetic operations for some positive constant c; see [**36**]. This estimate is close to that for the fastest factorization algorithms. Of course, it was obtained under some plausible assumptions.

When speaking about the complexity of the discrete logarithm problem, we usually mean the "general case". Indeed, even a large number can be easily factorized if the factors are small. An efficient discrete logarithm algorithm is known in the case where $p - 1$ is a product of small factors.

Let q be a prime dividing $p - 1$. We set $c \equiv a^{\frac{p-1}{q}} \mod p$. Then all residues $1, c, c^2, \ldots, c^{q-1}$ are distinct, and they are all solutions of the equation $x^q = 1$ in the field $\mathbb{F}_p = \mathbb{Z}/p\mathbb{Z}$. If q is not too large and an integer d satisfies the congruence $d^q \equiv 1 \mod p$, then it is easy to find the exponent u, $0 \le u < q$, such that $d \equiv c^u \mod p$, say, by an exhaustive search. The algorithm mentioned above is based on this property.

Suppose that $p - 1 = q^k h$, $(q, h) = 1$. The algorithm constructs consecutively integers u_j, $j = 1, \ldots, k$, such that

$$(23) \qquad \left(b^h a^{-hu_j}\right)^{q^{k-j}} \equiv 1 \mod p.$$

Since $b^{hq^k} \equiv 1 \mod p$, there is an integer u_1 such that $b^{hq^{k-1}} \equiv c^{u_1} \mod p$. Of course, congruence (23) holds for $j = 1$ and this u_1. Suppose a number u_j satisfying (23) is found. Then we define the exponent t by the congruence

$$(24) \qquad \left(b^h a^{-hu_j}\right)^{q^{k-j-1}} \equiv c^t \mod p$$

and set $u_{j+1} = u_j + tq^j$. Then

$$(25) \qquad \left(b^h a^{-hu_{j+1}}\right)^{q^{k-j-1}} \equiv c^t a^{-thq^{k-1}} \equiv 1 \mod p,$$

and congruence (23) for $j + 1$ follows.

In view of (22), for $j = k$ congruence (23) means that $a^{(x-u_k)h} \equiv 1 \mod p$. The integer a is a primitive root modulo p; therefore, $(x - u_k)h \equiv 0 \mod (p - 1)$, and we have

$$x \equiv u_k \mod q^k.$$

If $p - 1 = q_1^{k_1} \cdots q_s^{k_s}$, where all prime numbers q_j are small, then the procedure above allows one to find the residues $x \mod q_i^{k_i}$, $i =$

$1, \ldots, s$, and, using the Chinese Remainder Theorem, the residue x mod $(p-1)$, i.e., to solve congruence (22).

In the case of usual logarithms in the field of real numbers, there is a special base $e = 2.71828\ldots$, convenient for computing logarithms with arbitrary precision. This can be done, for example, by means of the rapidly converging series

$$(26) \qquad \ln \frac{1+x}{1-x} = 2\left(x + \frac{x^3}{3} + \frac{x^5}{5} + \cdots\right), \quad |x| < 1.$$

Logarithms with an arbitrary base c can be computed using the identity

$$(27) \qquad \log_c x = \frac{\log x}{\log c}.$$

In the case of discrete logarithms there is no special base. Nevertheless, the last formula relating logarithms with distinct bases remains true and allows one to choose a convenient base. The only requirement states that the logarithm $\mathrm{Log}\, c$ of the new base must be coprime with $p-1$. Then it is possible to divide modulo $p-1$ in (27). Note that this requirement is satisfied if and only if c is a primitive root. The generalized Riemann hypothesis implies that the smallest primitive root modulo p is not greater than $O(\log^6 p)$. Hence, we shall assume below that the base a in (22) is rather small, namely, $a = O(\log^6 p)$.

In the field $\mathbb{F}_p$, the discrete logarithms cannot be computed by considering limits (as in (26)), and we must use another approach. First of all, the required discrete logarithm $\mathrm{Log}\, b$ is computed not separately, but together with logarithms of some other numbers. Note that each congruence of the form

$$(28) \qquad q_1^{k_1} \cdots q_s^{k_s} \equiv q_1^{m_1} \cdots q_s^{m_s} \quad \mathrm{mod}\ p,$$

where $q_i, k_i, m_i \in \mathbb{Z}$, leads to the following relation between logarithms:

$$(29) \quad (k_1 - m_1)\mathrm{Log}\, q_1 + \cdots + (k_s - m_s)\mathrm{Log}\, q_s \equiv 0 \ \mathrm{mod}\ (p-1).$$

If congruences of the form

$$a \equiv q_1^{r_1} \cdots q_s^{r_s} \ \mathrm{mod}\ p, \quad b \equiv q_1^{x_1} \cdots q_s^{x_s} \ \mathrm{mod}\ p$$

hold, then

(30) $$r_1 \mathrm{Log}\, q_1 + \cdots + r_s \mathrm{Log}\, q_s \equiv 1 \mod (p-1)$$

and

(31) $$\mathrm{Log}\, b \equiv x_1 \mathrm{Log}\, q_1 + \cdots + x_s \mathrm{Log}\, q_s \mod (p-1).$$

Having sufficiently many vectors $k_1, \ldots, k_s, m_1, \ldots, m_s$ satisfying conditions (28) we can find a solution of the corresponding system of congruences (29) and (30). If the solution is unique, then it is precisely the set of logarithms $\mathrm{Log}\, q_1, \ldots, \mathrm{Log}\, q_s$, and we can find $\mathrm{Log}\, b$ by using (31).

We describe below the implementation of this idea presented in [20]. Some heuristics allowed the authors of [20] to claim that computing $\mathrm{Log}\, b$ with their algorithm requires $L^{1+\varepsilon}$ arithmetic operations, where $L = \exp(\sqrt{\log p \log \log p})$.

Let us set

$$H = [\sqrt{p}] + 1, \quad J = H^2 - p.$$

Then $0 < J < 2\sqrt{p} + 1$ and it is easy to verify that for any pair of integers c_1, c_2, the congruence

(32) $$(H + c_1)(H + c_2) \equiv J + (c_1 + c_2)H + c_1 c_2 \mod p$$

holds. If the numbers c_1, c_2 are not too large, say, $c_i \leq L^{1/2+\varepsilon}$ for some $\varepsilon > 0$, then the right-hand side of (32) is not greater than $p^{1/2+\varepsilon/2}$. It can be proved that a randomly chosen positive integer $x < p^{1/2+\varepsilon/2}$ is a product of two prime numbers smaller than $L^{1/2}$ with probability greater than $L^{-1/2-\varepsilon/2}$.

Denote by $S = \{q_1, \ldots, q_s\}$ the set of all prime numbers $q < L^{1/2}$ together with all prime numbers of the form $H + c$ for $0 < c < L^{1/2+\varepsilon}$. Then $s = O(L^{1/2+\varepsilon})$. Now, for a randomly chosen pair of elements of S, we try to factorize the corresponding expression on the right-hand side of (32). The factorization can be done, for example, by dividing by all prime numbers smaller than $L^{1/2}$. The above arguments show that after searching through all $\frac{1}{2}(L^{1/2+\varepsilon})^2 = O(L^{1+2\varepsilon})$ such pairs c_1, c_2 we obtain at least

(33) $$L^{-1/2-\varepsilon/2} \cdot O(L^{1+2\varepsilon}) = O(L^{1/2+3\varepsilon/2})$$

pairs such that the right-hand side of (32) has a decomposition into a product of prime factors all smaller than $L^{1/2}$. Thus, congruence (32) becomes of the form (28). This is how the system of equations of the form (29) is constructed.

Recall that by our assumption, the number a is significantly smaller than $L^{1/2}$. Therefore, it can be presented as a product of prime factors from the set $\{q_1, \ldots, q_s\}$, and we obtain congruence (30).

Note that the number (33) of congruences (29) found in this way is greater than s. Hence, the system of nonhomogeneous linear congruences in variables $\mathrm{Log}\, q_i$ thus constructed contains more congruences than variables. Of course, the set of its solutions can well be infinite. It is likely, however, that the system has, in fact, a unique solution, and this solution determines the discrete logarithms of all numbers q_i. This completes the first stage of the algorithm from [20].

As was mentioned earlier, each number on the right-hand side of (32) is not greater than $p^{1/2+\varepsilon/2}$. Therefore, it can be represented as a product of at most $O(\log p)$ prime factors, and therefore, each of the congruences (29) of the constructed system contains at most $O(\log p)$ nonzero coefficients. The matrix of the system of congruences is sparse, and its inversion can be done in a fewer number of operations than that required by the usual Gauss elimination method.

Instead of searching through all admissible values c_i, it is suggested in [20] to use the so-called sieve, which rejects all pairs of numbers such that the right-hand side of (32) cannot be presented as a product of small prime factors. For each c_1 and each small prime exponent $q' < L^{1/2}$ it is easy to find all solutions $c_2 < L^{1/2}$ of the linear congruence

$$J + (c_1 + c_2)H + c_1 c_2 \equiv 0 \mod q'.$$

When properly designed, this procedure also selects all required pairs c_1, c_2 and produces a factorization into prime factors of the right-hand sides of congruences (32).

After the execution of the first stage of the algorithm we obtain discrete logarithms for all numbers of the set S. The second stage reduces the computation of the discrete logarithm of b to the computation of logarithms of some numbers u not exceeding L^2. Probabilistic arguments show that choosing a random number w we can, after at most $L^{1/4}$ attempts, find w such that the residue $a^w b \bmod p$ can be represented as a product of prime numbers smaller than L^2. Let

$$a^w b \equiv \prod_{i=1}^{s} q_i^{y_i} \prod_{j=1}^{t} u_j^{z_j} \bmod p$$

be such a decomposition; here $u_1, \ldots, u_t$ are some prime numbers, $L^{1/2} < u_j < L^2$. The search for such a congruence takes $O(L^{1/2})$ arithmetic operations. As a result, the computation of the discrete logarithm of b is reduced to the computation of t discrete logarithms of the numbers u_j, $1 \le j \le t$, which are of middle size.

Finally, at the last stage the logarithms of all numbers u_j are computed. Let u be a prime number such that $L^{1/2} < u < L^2$. We set

$$G = \left[\frac{\sqrt{p}}{u} \right], \quad I = HGu - p.$$

For all integers $c_1, c_2 < L^{1/2+\varepsilon}$ the congruence

(34) $\qquad (H + c_1)(G + c_2)u \equiv I + (c_1 G + c_2 H + c_1 c_2)u \bmod p$

holds. Note that the right-hand side of this congruence is not greater than $p^{1/2} L^{5/2+\varepsilon}$. After sorting over all pairs c_1, c_2 from the interval specified above we can find such numbers that all prime factors of both $G + c_2$ and the right-hand side of congruence (34) are less than or equal to $L^{1/2}$. Then congruence (34) allows one to compute $\operatorname{Log} u$. The computation of $\operatorname{Log} b$ for known $\operatorname{Log} q_i$ takes $L^{1/2+\varepsilon}$ arithmetic operations.

There are other ways to construct relations (28). In [47] this construction is based on computations in algebraic number fields. Not only prime numbers, but also prime ideals with small norm are used there as factors in relations of type (28).

The discrete logarithm problem can be studied also in fields $\mathbb{F}_{p^n}$ consisting of p^n elements, in multiplicative groups of residue classes $(\mathbb{Z}/m\mathbb{Z})^*$, in groups of points of elliptic curves, and, more generally, in arbitrary groups. We refer the reader to [50] for further information.

9. Conclusion

In the present chapter we only briefly touched upon a few questions related to number-theoretic algorithms and their complexity estimates. We said nothing about a promising research in expanding sieve algorithms to algebraic number fields (number field sieves) and their applications to integer factorizing or discrete logarithm computing; see [**48**]. These are precisely the algorithms that give the upper estimate

$$\exp(c(\log N)^{1/3}(\log\log N)^{2/3})$$

for the factorization problem. We have not mentioned elliptic curves, that is, sets of the form

$$E_{a,b} = \{(x, y, z) \in (\mathbb{Z}/m\mathbb{Z})^3 \mid y^2 z = x^3 + axz^2 + bz^3\}$$

well defined up to an invertible common factor; these sets are endowed with a natural group structure. They can be used to construct rather efficient algorithms for integer factorizing and primality verification. In contrast to the multiplicative group $(\mathbb{Z}/m\mathbb{Z})^*$, the order of the group $E_{a,b}$ depends on a and b, and it may be different for the same value of m. This property turns out to be very useful, say, when factorizing m. Details on the usage of elliptic curves can be found in [**46**].

Chapter 5

Mathematics of Secret Sharing

1. Introduction

Consider the following, now standard, situation. Two people jointly own a piece of jewelry and want to put it into a safe deposit box. The modern safe deposit box has a 16-digit numeric code. Since the owners do not trust each other, they would like to lock the box in a way that would allow them to open it together, but not separately. To reach this goal, they invite a third person (a *dealer*) whom they both trust (say, because he will not have access to the box in the future). The dealer chooses a random sequence of 16 digits as the "key", closes the safe, and then passes the first 8 digits to the first owner and the last 8 digits to the second owner. From the point of view of common sense, this method seems to be optimal. Indeed, each owner receives "half the key". However, each of the owners left alone with the safe can find the half of the key he misses using a simple device searching through keys with frequency 1 MHz. It seems that the only way to improve the situation is to double the length of the key. Fortunately (in this case), mathematics suggests a different approach, which contradicts common sense. Namely, the dealer chooses two random sequences of 16 digits each, one for each of the owners, and calculates the key sequence by adding the respective digits of these two sequences modulo 10. It is more or less obvious (and we are going to prove this below) that all 10^{16} "keys" have the same probability for each of the owners, and the only way to find them is to search through all of them, which would require, in average, about a year and a half if we have a device generating keys with frequency 100 MHz.

The case of two participants is not sufficiently general from theoretical or practical point of view. Informally speaking, a "secret sharing scheme" (SSS) allows one to distribute a secret among n participants in such a way that only some admissible sets of participants would be able to reconstruct the secret, while any other set would not produce any additional information about the secret except for that known from the very beginning. (The tuple of admissible sets is called the access structure.) Such SSS's are called *perfect*, and we consider only perfect SSS's in the present chapter.

The history of SSS's starts in 1979, when this problem was posed and essentially solved by Blakley [**9**] and Shamir [**60**] for the case of so-called threshold (n, k)-SSS's (in this case all subsets of at least k elements are admissible). The so-called ideal SSS's are of the main interest; these are the SSS's such that the amount of information received by a participant is not greater than the "size" of the secret (we have already seen that this amount cannot be smaller). It turned out [**14**] that a matroid is associated to any such SSS (see the definition of a matroid in Section 4), and therefore, not each access structure determines an ideal secret sharing. On the other hand, it was shown that there exists a perfect SSS for each tuple of admissible sets, although the ways of constructing such an SSS are rather "inefficient". In the present chapter we discuss some algebro-geometric and combinatorial problems arising in the analysis of secret sharing schemes. Let us start with an example of such a problem.

We say that a family $(L_0, \ldots, L_n)$ of subspaces of a finite-dimensional vector space L over a field K satisfies the "everything or nothing" property if for each subset $A \subset \{1, \ldots, n\}$ the span of the subspaces $\{L_a, a \in A\}$ either contains the subspace L_0, or intersects L_0 only at $0 \in L_0$. We are going to show in Section 3 that a family with this property determines a "linear" SSS such that a set $A \subset \{1, \ldots, n\}$

is admissible if and only if the span of the subspaces $\{L_a, a \in A\}$ contains L_0. A number of questions arises in connection with this notion. Suppose, for example, that the field K is finite, $|K| = q$, and all subspaces $\{L_0, \ldots, L_n\}$ are one-dimensional; then what is the maximum number n of participants for linear threshold (n, k)-SSS's for a given $k > 1$? In other words, what is the maximum number of vectors $\{h_0, \ldots, h_n\}$ such that any k vectors whose span contains h_0 are linearly independent, while any $k + 1$ vectors with the same property are linearly dependent? It happens that this property is equivalent to the following one, which looks stronger, at least at first glance: any k vectors are linearly independent, while any $k + 1$ vectors are linearly dependent. Such systems of vectors were studied under the name of N-sets $(N = n+1)$ in finite projective geometry $PG(k-1, q)$, under the name of orthogonal tables of strength k and index $\lambda = 1$ in combinatorics, and under the name of verification matrices for the MDR-code in the coding theory (see details in [**49**]). In Section 3 we present a well-known construction of such sets with $N = q + 1$, and a rather old conjecture states that this value of N is exactly the maximum one except for two cases: the case of $q < k$, where $N = k + 1$, and the case of $q = 2^m$ and $k = 3$ or $k = q - 1$, where $N = q + 2$.

2. Secret sharing for arbitrary access structures

Let us start with a formal mathematical model. Suppose we have $n + 1$ sets $\mathcal{S}_0, \mathcal{S}_1, \ldots, \mathcal{S}_n$ and a (joint) probability distribution P on the direct product $\mathcal{S} = \mathcal{S}_0 \times \cdots \times \mathcal{S}_n$. Denote the corresponding random values by S_i. A set Γ of subsets of $\{1, \ldots, n\}$, called the access structure, is also given.

Definition 1. A pair $(P, \mathcal{S})$ is called a *perfect probabilistic SSS* realizing the access structure Γ if

$$(1) \qquad P(S_0 = c_0 \mid S_i = c_i, i \in A) \in \{0, 1\} \text{ for } A \in \Gamma,$$

$$(2) \qquad P(S_0 = c_0 \mid S_i = c_i, i \in A) = P(S_0 = c_0) \text{ for } A \notin \Gamma.$$

This definition can be interpreted as follows. There is a set $\mathcal{S}_0$ of all possible secrets; a secret $s_0 \in \mathcal{S}_0$ is chosen with probability $p(s_0)$; and there is an SSS that "distributes" the secret s_0 among

n participants by sending "projections" $s_1, \ldots, s_n$ of the secret with probability $P_{s_0}(s_1, \ldots, s_n)$. Note that the ith participant gets the projection $s_i \in \mathcal{S}_i$, but receives no information about the values of other projections, although he knows all sets $\mathcal{S}_i$ as well as both probability distributions $p(s_0)$ and $P_{s_0}(s_1, \ldots, s_n)$. These two distributions can be replaced with the single distribution $P(s_0, s_1, \ldots, s_n) = p(s_0)P_{s_0}(s_1, \ldots, s_n)$, see above. As was pointed out in the Introduction, the goals of SSS's are:

a) to allow the participants forming an admissible set A (that is, a set $A \in \Gamma$) together reconstruct the value of the secret (property (1));

b) to prevent participants forming a nonadmissible set A ($A \notin \Gamma$) from obtaining additional information about s_0; this means that the probability of reconstructing the secret value $S_0 = c_0$ must be independent of the "projections" S_i for $i \in A$ (property (2)).

A terminology remark. The "parts" of information sent to a participant of an SSS are called "shares" by Shamir and "shadows" by Blakley. The first name became the most popular one. The following example justifies the term "projection".

Example 1. Suppose the set $\mathcal{S}_0$ of all possible secrets is the set $\{0, 1, 2\}$ and the elements of this set are represented by a ball, a cube with edges parallel to the coordinate axes, and a cylinder with axis parallel to the z-axis. We assume that the diameter of the ball, the diameter of the cross section and the height of the cylinder, and the edge length of the cube, are all identical. The "part" of the first participant is the projection of the secret to the plane XY, while the "part" of the second is the projection to the plane XZ. Of course, the participants can reconstruct the secret together, but they are unable to do this separately. However, this SSS is not perfect since each of the participants gets some information about the secret: only two bodies from the given three can produce a given projection (say, if the projection is a square, then the projected body cannot be the ball).

One more remark. An element $x \in \{1, \ldots, n\}$ (a participant) is called *inessential* (with respect to the given Γ) if for an arbitrary nonadmissible set A the set $A \cup \{x\}$ is nonadmissible either. Obviously, there is no need to send any information to inessential participants. Therefore, without loss of generality, we consider only access structures Γ such that all elements are essential for them. Besides, it is natural to assume that Γ is a monotonic structure, that is, the assumptions $A \subset B$ and $A \in \Gamma$ imply that $B \in \Gamma$.

Example 2. Consider the simplest access structure, the (n, n)-threshold scheme; this means that all n participants together can reconstruct the secret, while an arbitrary proper subset of participants cannot obtain additional information about the secret. Let us try to construct an ideal SSS by choosing a secret and its projections from the set $\mathbb{Z}_q$ of residues modulo q, i.e., we set $\mathcal{S}_0 = \mathcal{S}_1 = \cdots = \mathcal{S}_n = \mathbb{Z}_q$. The dealer generates n independent random values x_i uniformly distributed over $\mathbb{Z}_q$ and sends to the ith participant $(i = 1, \ldots, n - 1)$ its "projection" $s_i = x_i$, while to the nth participant he sends the value $s_n = s_0 - (s_1 + \cdots + s_{n-1})$. The illusory "discrimination" of the nth participant disappears if we look at the distribution value $P_{s_0}(s_1, \ldots, s_n)$, which obviously is $1/q^{n-1}$ if $s_0 = s_1 + \cdots + s_n$, and is 0 otherwise. Now it is easy to verify property (2), which means, in this case, that the random value S_0 is independent of the random values $\{S_i : i \in A\}$ for an arbitrary proper subset A.

The definition of SSS given above uses the term "probability distribution". Below we give an almost equivalent combinatorial definition, which seems to be easier to understand. An arbitrary $M \times (n+1)$-matrix V with rows of the form $\mathbf{v} = (v_0, v_1, \ldots, v_n)$, $v_n \in \mathcal{S}_i$, is called the matrix of a combinatorial SSS, and its rows are called the "rules" for secret sharing. For a given value s_0 of the secret, the SSS dealer chooses randomly a row $\mathbf{v}$ with equal probability from the set of rows of V with the first element s_0.

Definition 2. A matrix V determines a *perfect combinatorial SSS* which realizes an access structure Γ if, first, for each set $A \in \Gamma$ the zero coordinate of each row of the matrix V is uniquely determined by the values of the coordinates in this row with indices in A and, second, for each set $A \notin \Gamma$ and arbitrary given values of coordinates with indices in A the number of rows of V with prescribed value α of the zero coordinate is independent of α.

To a perfect probabilistic SSS given by a pair $(P, \mathcal{S})$ we associate the matrix V whose rows $s \in \mathcal{S}$ are such that $P(s) > 0$. Note that

if we set all nonzero values of P in Definition 1 equal to each other
and reformulate conditions (1) and (2) in the combinatorial language,
then we obtain Definition 2. This combinatorial definition can be
generalized slightly if we allow identical rows in the matrix V. The
generalized definition is equivalent to Definition 1 with rational values
of the probabilities $P(s)$.

Example 2 (continued). Let us reformulate the construction of an
(n, n)-threshold SSS above in the combinatorial language. The rows
of the matrix V are all vectors $\mathbf{s}$ such that $-s_0 + s_1 + \cdots + s_n = 0$. Obviously, the matrix V determines a perfect combinatorial SSS
for $\Gamma = \{1, \ldots, n\}$ since for any proper subset $A \subset \{1, \ldots, n\}$ and
arbitrary given values of coordinates in the set A the number of rows
of V with a given value of the zero coordinate is $q^{n-1-|A|}$.

Although this seems strange, but using the simple scheme of Example 2 as the main block, we can construct a perfect SSS for arbi-
trary access structure. Namely, we can realize the threshold $(|A|, |A|)$-
SSS described above independently for all admissible sets, that is, for
$A \in \Gamma$, and send to the ith participant the projections s_i^A for each
set A he belongs to. It is easy to translate this informal description
into the combinatorial language of properties of V and verify that
this SSS is perfect. As it often happens, the word "perfect" does not
mean "efficient", and the size of the "projection" in this SSS is usually
much greater than the size of the secret. This scheme can be made
much more efficient since it suffices to realize the threshold $(|A|, |A|)$-
SSS's only for the minimal admissible sets A, i.e., for $A \in \Gamma_{\min}$, where
$\Gamma_{\min}$ is the set of all minimal (with respect to inclusion) sets from Γ.
Nevertheless, the size (say, in bits) of the "projection" for a threshold
$(n, n/2)$-SSS is $\binom{n}{n/2} \sim 2^n/\sqrt{2\pi n}$ times larger than the size of the secret (this is the worst case for the above construction). On the other
hand, as we are going to verify later, any threshold access structure
admits an ideal realization, i.e., it can be realized as an SSS with the
same sizes of the secret and the "projections". Thus, the problem
arises, what is the maximum possible ratio of the size of the "projection" and the size of the secret for the worst access structure with the
best implementation? Formally, we set $R(n) = \max R(\Gamma)$, where the
maximum is taken over all access structures with n participants, and

$R(\Gamma) = \min\max \frac{\log|S_i|}{\log|S_0|}$, where the minimum is taken over all SSS's realizing the given access structure Γ, and the maximum is taken over all $i = 1, \ldots, n$. The above construction shows that $R(n) \leq \binom{n}{n/2}$. On the other hand, it was proved recently in [**23**] that $R(n) \geq n/\log n$. Such a huge gap between the upper and lower estimates gives further research full scope (we conjecture that $R(n)$ grows exponentially in n).

3. Linear secret sharing

We start with the elegant secret sharing scheme for threshold access structures suggested by Shamir [**60**]. Let $K = \mathbb{F}_q$ be the finite field of q elements (for example, we can assume that $q = p$ is a prime number, and $K = \mathbb{Z}_p$) and take $n < q$. We assign to each of the n participants nonzero elements $\{a_1, \ldots, a_n\}$ of the field, and set $a_0 = 0$. When sharing a secret, the dealer of the SSS generates $k - 1$ independent random values f_j $(j = 1, \ldots, k-1)$ uniformly distributed over $\mathbb{F}_q$ and sends the value $s_i = f(a_i)$ to the ith participant; here f is the polynomial $f(x) = f_0 + f_1 x + \cdots + f_{k-1} x^{k-1}$, where $f_0 = s_0$. Since an arbitrary polynomial of degree $k - 1$ can be uniquely reconstructed from its values at arbitrary k points (say, by the Lagrange interpolation formula), any k participants together can reconstruct the polynomial f and find the secret as the value $s_0 = f(0)$. For the same reason, for arbitrary $k-1$ participants, arbitrary values s_i of the projections they receive, and an arbitrary secret s_0, there is exactly one polynomial f such that $s_i = f(a_i)$ for all i. Hence, this scheme is perfect, by Definition 2. The "linearity" of this scheme becomes obvious if we write the secret sharing in the matrix form:

$$(3) \qquad\qquad\qquad \mathbf{s} = \mathbf{f}H,$$

where $\mathbf{s} = (s_0, \ldots, s_n)$, $\mathbf{f} = (f_0, \ldots, f_{k-1})$, the $k \times (n + 1)$-matrix H has the form $H = (h_{ij}) = (a_i^{j-1})$ and $h_{00} = 1$. Note that any k columns of this matrix are linearly independent, and the maximum possible number of columns of H is q; in order to reach the value $q+1$ promised in Section 1 we must add the column corresponding to the point at infinity.

Exercise. Figure out how this can be done.

Let us take, for H in (3), an arbitrary $r \times (n+1)$-matrix with elements from K. We call the resulting SSS a *linear one-dimensional SSS*. It is a perfect combinatorial SSS with the access structure Γ consisting of sets A such that the vector $\mathbf{h}_0$ can be expressed as a linear combination of the vectors $\{\mathbf{h}_j : j \in A\}$, where $\mathbf{h}_j$ is the jth column of the matrix H. We see from (3) that the rows of the matrix V corresponding to this SSS are linear combinations of the rows of H. Let us rewrite (3) in the form

$$s_j = (\mathbf{f}, \mathbf{h}_j) \text{ for } j = 0, 1, \ldots, n,$$

where $(\mathbf{f}, \mathbf{h}_j)$ is the inner product of the vectors $\mathbf{f}$ and $\mathbf{h}_j$. If $A \in \Gamma$, i.e., $\mathbf{h}_0 = \sum \lambda_j \mathbf{h}_j$, then

$$s_0 = (\mathbf{f}, \mathbf{h}_0) = (\mathbf{f}, \sum \lambda_j \mathbf{h}_j) = \sum \lambda_j (\mathbf{f}, \mathbf{h}_j) = \sum \lambda_j s_j,$$

whence the value of the secret can be uniquely reconstructed from its "projections". Now suppose the vector $\mathbf{h}_0$ cannot be presented as a linear combination of the vectors $\{\mathbf{h}_j : j \in A\}$. We want to show that in this case for arbitrary given values of the coordinates from the set A, the number of rows of the matrix V with a prescribed value of the zero coordinate is independent of this value. This can be easily verified if we treat equation (3) as a system of linear equations with respect to the variables f_i and use the fact that the system is compatible if and only if the rank of the matrix of coefficients is equal to the rank of the extended matrix of coefficients and all compatible systems have the same number of solutions, which coincides with the number of solutions of a homogeneous system.

Hint. Consider two systems: one without the "zero equation" (that is, without the free term), and the other with it. Since the vector $\mathbf{h}_0$ cannot be represented as a linear combination of the vectors $\{\mathbf{h}_j : j \in A\}$, the rank of the coefficient matrix of the second system exceeds the rank of the coefficient matrix of the first system by one. This fact implies immediately that if the first system is compatible, then the same is true for the second system for an arbitrary s_0 as well.

This construction suggests the following definition of a general linear SSS. Suppose the secret and its "projections" are represented as finite-dimensional vectors $\mathbf{s}_i = (s_i^1, \ldots, s_i^{m_i})$ produced by the formulas $\mathbf{s}_i = \mathbf{f}H_i$, where H_i are some $r \times m_i$-matrices. Associate to each matrix H_i the vector space L_i spanned by its columns (i.e., the space of linear combinations of the column vectors of H_i). An easy argument similar to that for the one-dimensional case above (all $m_i = 1$) shows that this construction leads to a perfect SSS if and only if the family of vector subspaces $\{L_0, \ldots, L_n\}$ of the finite-dimensional vector space K^r possesses the "everything or nothing" property mentioned in the Introduction. Then the set A is admissible ($A \in \Gamma$) if and only if the span of the spaces $\{L_a : a \in A\}$ contains the entire space L_0. On the other hand, the set A is nonadmissible ($A \notin \Gamma$) if and only if the span of the subspaces $\{L_a : a \in A\}$ intersects L_0 merely in the origin. Note that were the intersection of L_0 with the span of $\{L_a : a \in A\}$ nontrivial for some A, the participants of A would be able to obtain some additional information about A, which nevertheless would not allow them to reconstruct the secret; this means, of course, that the scheme would not be perfect.

Example 3. Consider the access structure $\Gamma_{\min} = \{\{1, 2\}, \{2, 3\}, \{3, 4\}\}$ for four participants. This was the first example of an access structure without an ideal realization. Moreover, it was proved that $R(\Gamma) \geq 3/2$ for an arbitrary perfect realization of this structure. On the other hand, it can be verified directly that the matrices $H_0, H_1, \ldots, H_4$ in Table 1 determine a perfect linear SSS with $R = 3/2$, which realizes this structure. Therefore, this SSS is optimal (most efficient).

4. Ideal secret sharing and matroids

We start with the definition of an ideal SSS. Let us return to the definition of a perfect SSS. The following definition of a perfect SSS from [**14**] is even more general than the probabilistic Definition 1 since the property (2) is replaced there with a weaker one.

For an arbitrary set $B \subseteq \{0, 1, \ldots, n\}$, we denote by V_B the $M \times |B|$-matrix obtained from V by selecting the columns with indices belonging to B. Denote the number of pairwise distinct rows in a matrix W by $\|W\|$.

Table 1

$$
H_0 = \begin{bmatrix} 1 & 0 \\ 0 & 1 \\ 0 & 0 \\ 0 & 0 \\ 0 & 0 \\ 0 & 0 \end{bmatrix}, \quad
H_1 = \begin{bmatrix} 0 & 0 \\ 0 & 0 \\ 1 & 0 \\ 0 & 1 \\ 0 & 0 \\ 0 & 0 \end{bmatrix}, \quad
H_2 = \begin{bmatrix} 1 & 0 & 0 \\ 0 & 1 & 0 \\ 1 & 0 & 0 \\ 0 & 1 & 0 \\ 0 & 0 & 1 \\ 0 & 0 & 0 \end{bmatrix},
$$

$$
H_3 = \begin{bmatrix} 0 & 0 & 1 \\ 0 & 0 & 0 \\ 0 & 0 & 0 \\ 0 & 1 & 0 \\ 0 & 0 & 1 \\ 1 & 0 & 0 \end{bmatrix}, \quad
H_4 = \begin{bmatrix} 0 & 0 \\ 0 & 1 \\ 0 & 0 \\ 0 & 0 \\ 1 & 0 \\ 0 & 1 \end{bmatrix}.
$$

Definition 3. A matrix V determines a BD-perfect[1] SSS realizing an access structure Γ if

$$
(4) \qquad\qquad \|V_{A \cup \{0\}}\| = \|V_A\| \cdot \|V_0\|^{\delta_\Gamma(A)},
$$

where $\delta_\Gamma(A) = 0$ if $A \in \Gamma$, and $\delta_\Gamma(A) = 1$ otherwise.

The assumption on nonadmissible sets A in this definition is much weaker than that in Definitions 1 and 2; namely, we require that if the set of rows of V with given values of coordinates belonging to A is nonempty, then the zero coordinate of these rows must take all possible values of the secret (without requiring "with the same multiplicity" as in the combinatorial Definition 2, or "with the same a probability" as in the probabilistic Definition 1). It is easy to show that the matrix of an arbitrary perfect probabilistic SSS determines a BD-perfect SSS, but the converse is false.

For an arbitrary combinatorial SSS given by a matrix V, let us consider on sets $A \subseteq \{0, 1, \ldots, n\}$ the function $h(A) = \log_q \|V_A\|$, where $q = |\mathcal{S}_0|$. It can be easily verified that $\max\{h(A), h(B)\} \leq h(A \cup B) \leq h(A) + h(B)$ for any two sets A and B, and condition (4)

---

[1] The letters BD here stand for Brickell and Davenport who suggested this notion. (*Added in translation.*)

can be rewritten in the form

$$h_q(V_{A \cup \{0\}}) = h_q(V_A) + \delta_\Gamma(A) h_q(V_0).$$

Lemma. *For any BD-perfect SSS, the following holds: if $A \notin \Gamma$ and $\{A \cup i\} \in \Gamma$, then*

$$h(i) \geq h(0).$$

Proof. By the assumptions of the lemma, $h(A \cup \{0\}) = h(A) + h(0)$, and $h(A \cup \{i\} \cup \{0\}) = h(A \cup \{i\})$. Therefore,

$$h(A) + h(i) \geq h(A \cup \{i\}) = h(A \cup \{i\} \cup \{0\})$$
$$\geq h(A \cup \{0\}) = h(A) + h(0).$$

$\square$

Since we assumed that all elements $i \in \{1, \ldots, n\}$ are essential, i.e., for any i there is a subset A such that $A \notin \Gamma$ and $\{A \cup \{i\}\} \in \Gamma$, the lemma immediately implies the following

Corollary. *For an arbitrary BD-perfect SSS we have $|\mathcal{S}_i| \geq |\mathcal{S}_0|$ for all $i = 1, \ldots, n$.*

This corollary means that, as we already mentioned at the beginning of the chapter, the "size" of a projection for perfect SSS's cannot be less than the "size" of the secret. That is why a BD-perfect SSS is called ideal if $|\mathcal{S}_i| = |\mathcal{S}_0|$ for all $I = 1, \ldots, n$.

Remark. The inequality $|\mathcal{S}_i| \geq |\mathcal{S}_0|$ is valid for perfect probabilistic SSS's as well since their matrices determine BD-perfect SSS's.

Now we have the following natural question: what are the access structures Γ such that there exist ideal (either probabilistic or combinatorial) SSS's realizing them? As was already mentioned in the introduction, the best currently known answer uses the notion of a matroid. Recall the definition of a matroid and some properties of these objects.

A *matroid* is a finite set X together with a family I of its subsets which are called independent (all other subsets are dependent), satisfying the following conditions:

(5_1) $\emptyset \in I$;

(5_2) if $A \in I$ and $B \subset A$, then $B \in I$;

(5_3) if $A, B \in I$ and $|A| = |B| + 1$,

                then there exists $a \in A \setminus B$ such that $a \cup B \in I$.

Example 4. The set X is a set of vectors in a vector space, while an independent subsets are the subsets of linearly independent vectors.

The theory of matroids started, in fact, with this example as an attempt to formalize "intrinsic" properties of linear dependence. Fortunately, this attempt failed since there are matroids that cannot be realized in this way (i.e., as systems of vectors), and the theory of matroids spread far beyond linear algebra; see [**64**].

Example 5 (Vamos matroid). Consider the set $X = \{1, 2, 3, 4, 5, 6, 7, 8\}$ and put $a = \{1, 2\}$, $b = \{3, 4\}$, $c = \{5, 6\}$, and $d = \{7, 8\}$. In the Vamos matroid, all sets $a \cup c$, $a \cup d$, $b \cup c$, $b \cup d$, $c \cup d$, as well as all sets containing 5 or more elements, are dependent, while all other subsets of X are independent. It is known that this matroid is not linear.

Matroids can also be defined using the so-called rank functions. The rank function of a matroid is the function r on the subsets of X whose value on a set $A \subset X$ is equal to the maximal cardinality of an independent subset $B \subseteq A$. Obviously, $r(A) = |A|$ exactly on independent subsets. The rank function has the following properties:

(6_1) $r(A) \in \mathbb{Z}, \quad r(\emptyset) = 0$;

(6_2) $r(A) \leq r(A \cup \{b\}) \leq r(A) + 1$;

(6_3) if $r(A \cup \{b\}) = r(A \cup \{C\}) = r(A)$,

                then $r(A \cup \{b\} \cup \{c\}) = r(A)$.

Conversely, suppose a function r possesses properties (6_1)–(6_3). We declare the subsets A such that $r(A) = |A|$ independent. Then these subsets determine a matroid, and r is the rank function for this matroid. It is also possible to define a matroid in terms of minimal dependent subsets, called *cycles*. A matroid is called *connected* if for any pair of its elements there is a cycle containing both these elements.

Now we can formulate the main result.

Theorem (see [**14**]). *For a BD-perfect SSS realizing an access structure Γ the independent sets defined by the condition $\log_{|\mathcal{S}_0|} \|V_A\| = |A|$ determine a connected matroid on the set $\{0, 1, \ldots, n\}$. All cycles of this matroid containing the element 0 have the form $\{0\} \cup A$, where $A \in \Gamma_{\min}$.*

The main step in the proof of this theorem is the "verification" of the fact that the function $h(\cdot)$ takes integer values. Indeed, the other properties (6_1)–(6_3) are obvious for h, whence it determines a matroid provided it takes integer values. The proof of the theorem and of some more general statements can be found in [**10**].

Note that the second part of the theorem implies that distinct ideal SSS's realizing the same access structure are always associated to the same matroid since the matroid is uniquely determined by all cycles passing through a given element (see [**64**]). Hence, a matroid is associated to each access structure admitting an ideal realization, and this matroid is unique.

A number of natural questions arise in connection with this theorem. First of all, do the ideal SSS's generate all matroids? The answer is negative; indeed, the Vamos matroid cannot be obtained as the matroid of an ideal SSS [**59**]. On the other hand, linear matroids are precisely the ideal one-dimensional linear SSS's studied in Section 3. Now we can ask whether there is an access structure Γ that cannot be realized by an ideal one-dimensional SSS, but admits an ideal multidimensional linear SSS realization. Such an example was constructed recently in [**6**], whence the class of multidimensional linear matroids is more general than that of one-dimensional linear matroids.

Thus, the class of ideal SSS's contains the class of linear matroids, but there are matroids that cannot be realized by ideal SSS's. To analyze the differences between these classes seems to be a complicated task. In particular, does there exist an access structure Γ that admits an ideal realization but cannot be realized by an ideal linear multidimensional SSS?

Chapter 6

Cryptography Olympiads for High School Students

1. Introduction

Suppose you want to send a message to a receiver in such a way that its contents remains secret to anybody else. There are at least two possible ways to do this. First, you may try to use methods related to *steganography* (invisible ink, microphotographs, etc.), i.e., to conceal the very existence of a secret message. The other possibility is to disguise the meaning of the message so that an unauthorized person who just occasionally or deliberately reads your message cannot understand it. In this case you can use the methods of cryptography. The word *cryptography* stems from the two Greek roots: "$\kappa\rho\upsilon\pi\tau o\varsigma$", secret, and "$\gamma\rho\alpha\varphi\omega$", to write. Thus *cryptography* is the art of disguising the substance of a message. The message that you want to transmit to the receiver is called the *plaintext*. For example, in Problem 2.5 (in the Problems section) one of the plaintexts is THEREARETWOQUESTIONSLEFT. To keep the message a secret it is transformed, by using a method of cryptography, before transmission. The transformed message is called a *ciphertext* or a *cryptogram*.

In Problem 2.5, the cryptogram reads

WQUZJSUNJETIXNIBNGQB

A cryptogram is not necessarily a sequence of letters. It may look as numeric data, or a sequence of special symbols (*dancing men*). The operation of transformation of a plaintext into a cryptogram is known as *enciphering* or *encryption*. The receiver is a priori informed how to recover the message from the cryptogram. The process of translation from the ciphertext to the plaintext is known as *deciphering* or *decryption*. The encryption algorithm must be so chosen that another person (who does not know the algorithm) cannot understand the message. If this condition is satisfied, the meaning of your message is safely concealed. For convenience, denote the plaintext by A, and the cryptogram by B. Let f stand for the operation of encryption and g for decryption. The transformation of a plaintext A to a cryptogram B can be written as $f(A) = B$ and the inverse transformation (the determination of the plaintext from the cryptogram) as $g(B) = A$.

The algorithm f cannot be arbitrary. It must satisfy the condition that using the cryptogram B and the inverse transformation g, the receiver can uniquely determine the plaintext. Encryption algorithms are divided into a number of groups. Two algorithms of the same group differ only in the value of a certain parameter. This parameter can be a number, a table, or anything else. In cryptography, a value of the parameter is called *a key*. Thus, by specifying the key value, we select one particular algorithm from the group.

Why do we need the concept of a key? There are at least two reasons for this. First, the process of encryption is implemented, as a rule, through the use of special devices. The device is controlled by some input parameters. You can change the parameters to prevent your messages from being deciphered by another person who has the same device but does not know the parameters you have set. Second, repeated use of the same algorithm f can allow an interceptor to learn how to reconstruct the plaintext from a cryptogram without determining the inverse transformation g. Therefore, it is a good idea to change the encryption algorithm from time to time.

Using the notion of a key, we can write the operation of encryption as follows:

$$f_\alpha(A) = B,$$

where α denotes the key known to both the sender and the receiver.

For each α, the transformation f_α must have an inverse transformation, g_α, which uniquely recovers the plaintext A from the cryptogram B and the key α:

$$g_\alpha(B) = A.$$

The set of all keys together with the corresponding transformations f_α is called a *cipher*.

Among all of the ciphers the following are of special importance: *substitution ciphers* and *transposition ciphers*.

A transposition cipher leaves the characters the same, but changes their order. For example, a cipher can swap each letter at an even position in the plaintext and the letter immediately to the left of it. It is clear that the letters of the ciphertext coincide with those of the plaintext.

A substitution cipher replaces each character in a plaintext with another character to obtain the ciphertext. The order of characters in the plaintext coincides with the order of their ciphertext equivalents in the cryptogram. A simple example of a substitution cipher is as follows. Each letter in the plaintext is replaced with its position number in the alphabet. A sequence of letters is transformed into a sequence of numbers.

As a rule, in Olympiad problems the encryption algorithm is known, but the key is not. To recover the plaintext from a ciphertext, one can either 1) find the key and determine the plaintext straightforwardly, or 2) find the plaintext without determining the key. In contrast to the process of deciphering (the key is known), the determination of the plaintext without using the key is called *breaking the cipher*. Olympiads' winners have clearly shown that in most problems the ciphers are breakable.

Different ciphers offer different degrees of security; it depends on how hard they are to break. Almost universally, the following rule, first formulated by the Dutchman A. Kerckhoffs (1835–1903), is adopted: the entire mechanism of encryption, except for the value of the secret key, is known to the enemy cryptanalyst. A natural characteristic of a cipher is the number of possible keys. We can break the cipher by trying all possible keys consecutively. As noted above, the statements of most Olympiad problems, in accordance with Kerckhoffs's rule, include an explicit description of the encryption algorithm, but not of the key. For instance, solving Problem 4.4 one can try each of the 24 possible keys one by one until a meaningful text appears. Even though the plaintext was in Latin, many competitors (with no knowledge of Latin) have managed to recover it.

Encryption is often confused with *coding*. As mentioned above, encryption implies the use of an encryption algorithm and a secret key. On the contrary, there is nothing secret in coding. We replace the letters (or the whole words) of the plaintext by some special characters. Codes are not designed to conceal the substance of a message but to represent it in a form more suitable for transmission, or, maybe, to shorten messages, etc. Therefore, a code can be thought of as a substitution cipher with a single key. For example, Morse code ciphers "a" into "●━", and there is no secret in it.

Nowadays, electronic cryptographic devices are widely used to protect information. An important characteristic of such a device is not only the level of security it offers but also the speed at which it implements encryption and decryption. To design or to use such a device appropriately, one should be familiar with recent advances in cryptography, the science based on mathematics, physics, computer science, electronics, etc.

Contemporary cryptography is a rapidly developing area. New branches constantly appear in it. The so called *public key cryptosystems* have been developing since 1976. The main peculiarity about them is that the key used for encryption is different from the key used for decryption. The encryption key can be made public and even printed in an ordinary phone book along with the phone number and home address of its owner. A detailed discussion of public key cryptosystems can be found in Chapters 1–3.

The term *cryptology*, along with the word *cryptography* is encountered in the literature. It is derived from the Greek words "hidden" and "word". This is an umbrella term used to describe the entire field of secret communication.

Cryptology splits into two parts: cryptography and cryptanalysis. A cryptographer seeks methods to keep messages secure. The task of a cryptanalyst is exactly the opposite: to recover the message without knowing the key. If the cryptanalyst succeeds, he is said to have broken the cipher, whereas in fact he has just found the key for the encryption algorithm known to him a priori.

2. Substitution ciphers

At present, the so-called *substitution ciphers* are among the most frequently used ciphers. Substitution ciphers replace blocks (letters, words, etc.) of a plaintext by symbols that can be letters, words, numbers, or what not. Of course, the substitution is to be made in such a way that the plaintext can be recovered from the ciphertext uniquely.

Suppose we encrypt a message by replacing each letter of the message with another symbol. Formally, this can be described as follows. For each letter α of the plaintext we have a set of symbols M_α such that for $\alpha \neq \beta$ the intersection of the sets M_α and M_β is empty. The set M_α consists of all possible ciphertext equivalents of the letter α. The table

(1)

a	b	c	$\ldots$	z
M_a	M_b	M_c	$\ldots$	M_z

is the key for the substitution cipher. Using this table one can do both encryption and decryption.

To encrypt a message, we replace each letter α of the message by a symbol from M_α. It is clear that identical letters of the plaintext could be replaced by different symbols. Thus, the use of the key (1) may result in different ciphertexts for the same plaintext. Consider, for example, the key

A	B	C	D	E	F	G	H	I	J	K	L	M	N	O	P
21	37	14	22	01	24	62	73	46	23	12	08	27	53	35	04
40	26	63	47	31	83	88	30	02	91	72	32	77	68	60	44
10	03	71	82	15	70	11	55	90	69	38	61	54	09	84	45

Q	R	S	T	U	V	W	X	Y	Z
20	13	59	25	75	43	19	29	06	65
52	39	07	49	33	85	58	80	50	34
89	67	93	76	18	51	87	66	81	92

Then each of the texts

4672536019073337077646251849026068149044430313959

9038096087071826934990493376023509630204730113307

is a valuable cryptogram for the plaintext

IKNOWSUBSTITUTIONCIPHERS

Since the sets $M_a, \ldots, M_z$ are pairwise disjoint, any symbol of a ciphertext belongs to exactly one of these sets; hence no ambiguity occurs when recovering the plaintext from a ciphertext.

Typically, M_α is a one-element set. For example, in the novel *Journey to the Centre of the Earth* by J. Verne, professor Lindenbrock came across a parchment with runic characters. Each set M_α consists of a single element. The elements were of the kind

(2)

In Arthur Conan Doyle's short story *The Dancing Men*, the elements were fancifully looking dancing figures

(3)

At first sight, it may seem that the more tricky the elements look, the harder it is to break the cipher. Obviously, this is not true. To each peculiar character we can uniquely assign a letter (or a number) and thus obtain a cryptogram composed of letters (numbers). In J. Verne's novel *Journey to the Centre of the Earth*, each runic character was replaced by a letter of the German alphabet and that simplified the reconstruction of the message. To a cryptanalyst it is evident that the use of strange symbols alone does not make a cipher more secure. It is more convenient, however, to deal with cryptograms composed of letters and digits.

Consider some examples of substitution ciphers. Let each set M_α consist of a single letter. For example,

(4)

а	б	в	г	д	е	ж	з	и	к	л	м	н	о	п	р
г	л	ь	п	д	р	а	м	ц	в	э	ъ	х	о	б	н

с	т	у	ф	х	ц	ч	ш	щ	ъ	ы	ь	э	ю	я
с	ж	я	и	ю	к	щ	ф	е	у	ы	ч	ш	т	а

Such a cipher is also referred to as *a simple substitution cipher* or, *monoalphabetic cipher*. By the use of the key (4), both decryption and encryption are performed easily. For encryption, each letter of the message is replaced with the letter exactly beneath it in the table (e.g., а is replaced with г). For decryption, г is replaced with а, etc. Therefore, the actual key of the cipher is the second row in (4) and only this row needs be memorized for encryption-decryption operations.

At the same time, it is hard to remember a random sequence of letters. That is why the second row in (4) is usually formed following some rule.

As far as it is known, Julius Caesar was the first man who used a substitution cipher. In this cipher, the letters in the second row of the table (4) are written in the alphabetic order but the first letter is not а:

(5)

а	б	в	...	ь	э	ю	я
г	д	е	...	я	а	б	в

In Problem 4.4, the Caesar cipher is used. To determine the key, it is sufficient to know the first letter in the second row. (Of course, the alphabetic order of the letters is assumed to be known.) The Caesar cipher has a serious weak point: the number of possible keys coincides with the number of letters in the alphabet. Trying all of them, we readily find an intelligible text. Usually, the other texts make no sense. This is the case in Problem 4.4, where the task is to determine a message in Latin.

A cipher alphabet (the second row in (4)) can be formed upon use of *a keyword*. Let our keyword be *keyboard*. To construct the cipher alphabet, we write out the keyword and then write out the remaining letters of the alphabet in the lexicographical order. We have

KEYBOARDCFGHIJLMNPQSTUVWXZ

It is clear that the number of keys far exceeds the number of letters in the alphabet.

A serious drawback of substitution ciphers is that if a letter appears in a plaintext frequently, then the corresponding letter (symbol) appears in the ciphertext equally frequently. Hence, cryptanalysis of this kind of ciphers starts with the assumption that most frequently appearing letters in the cryptogram correspond to most frequently appearing letters in ordinary texts. If a ciphertext is long enough, the frequency analysis solves the problem completely.

In addition to the frequency analysis, there are other approaches that can help to recover the message, e.g., the task is simplified considerably if the breaks between words and punctuation are known (see Problem 4.2). In this case, considering short words (definite and indefinite articles, prepositions, conjunctions), we can guess the values of certain characters of the cipher alphabet. Special attention is to be paid to double characters of the ciphertext because they correspond to tt, ll, ee, etc.

Success in dealing with substitution ciphers is a matter of perseverance and luck. There are no formal rules for breaking such ciphers.

The cryptogram in Problem 1.5 (such cryptograms are popular among schoolchildren) represents a substitution cipher with the key

0	1	2	3	4	5	6	7	8	9
d	e	c	r	y	p	t	i	o	n

Here numbers are assigned to letters so as to make some arithmetical expressions valid. Therefore, the main principle behind breaking the cipher is the analysis of those expressions, not the frequency analysis.

It follows from the discussion above that a substitution cipher can be easily broken through the analysis of a comparatively small portion of a ciphertext. Therefore, the efforts were made to improve the security level of substitution ciphers. It was suggested, for example, that some letters of a plaintext be replaced with two characters and some with one character. For instance, let A be 73 and let B be 7. Writing a ciphertext with no breaks between characters obviously provides additional difficulties for an enemy cryptanalyst because it is not clear how many plaintext letters the ciphertext 737 represents.

Another way to improve the security is to use sets M_α with more than one element in each. Such ciphers are called *multiple-substitution ciphers* or *homophonic ciphers*. Homophonic ciphers hide the natural frequency distribution of letters thus complicating the cryptanalysis. A serious difficulty with this sort of ciphers is the need of memorizing the key, which is much longer than the alphabet (it includes a number of possible substitutes for each plaintext letter). From spy movies we know that during the World War II ciphers based on the use of books were employed. The correspondents possessing the same book used it to indicate the letters of the message by means of numbers referring to specific letters in the book. A cipher equivalent of a letter was a group of five digits representing the page (the first two digits), the line (the third digit), and the position of the letter in the line (the other digits). This is the reason why immediately after capturing a spy, efforts were made to find the book the spy used.

In addition to the examples of substitution ciphers considered above, more complicated substitution ciphers also exist. Still the examples already considered clearly show the great diversity of substitution ciphers. At the same time, all these ciphers share the same weak point, that is, possessing a long enough message encrypted under the same key, an enemy cryptanalyst would break the cipher easily. For this reason, substitution ciphers are used in combination with other types of ciphers, especially with *transposition ciphers* discussed below.

In conclusion, consider examples of breaking substitution ciphers encountered in literature. Besides purely linguistic facts, pay attention to other unexpected reasons and considerations employed in

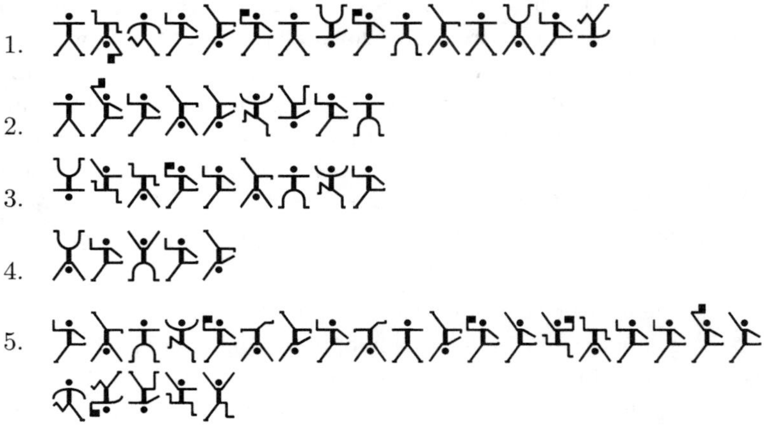

1.

2.

3.

4.

5.

Figure 1

breaking the ciphers. These examples again confirm that cracking of ciphers is an art.

A. Conan Doyle, *The Dancing Men.* In this story, Holmes had to read the five messages shown in Figure 1.

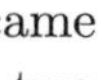

It is important that Holmes began his analysis having at his disposal only the first message; the others came later. From inspection of the first message, Holmes had made two important conclusions that were then confirmed by the other messages. The first conclusion was that men bearing flags were used to break up the sentences into words. The second was that the symbol 🏃 stood for E. Indeed, in English texts, the letter E predominates all other letters. The first message was 15 letters long and contained four identical symbols so it was reasonable to assume these symbols to be E. But from that point on he could do no more because, for example, letters T, A, O and I appear in English texts with almost equal frequency; it would have been an endless task to try all possible combinations. After getting the second and third messages, Holmes managed to advance further. The fourth message contained two E's and no flags, hence it was a single word. It could be "sever", "never", "fever", or what not. Holmes realized that this was an answer to an appeal and, consequently, the word was "never". Having accepted that as correct, Holmes got the figures that stood for N, V, R. But even then he was in a difficult situation. It was a happy thought that unmasked a few more letters. The appeal was addressed to Elsie, a young lady living in the house where all this happened. The end of the third message with two letters E and three letters between them stood for her name very well. By that, Holmes got L, S, and I. The four-letter word that preceeded the word ELSIE ended in E and it definitely was COME (nothing else fit). He became in possession of C, O, and M. With all the information accumulated, the first message looked

.M .ERE ..E SL.NE.

where dots stood for yet unknown letters. The first letter was readily found to be A because it appeared no fewer than three times in that short sentence. The first message became

AM .ERE A.E SLANE.

With so many letters known, Holmes proceeded with the second message

A. ELRI.ES.

To make sense, only T and G could be put for missing letters. That was the name of a hotel or inn at which the writer was staying. Being aware that in her earlier life the lady had spent a lot of time in America, Holmes decided that the writer (her lover maybe) was an American. Then there was every reason to assume that the writer's name was Abe Slaney. Working with known letters, the last message took the form

ELSIE .RE.ARE TO MEET THY GO.

The addition of P and D completed that threat. After that, Holmes wrote to the bastard the following:

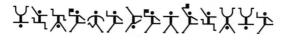

Edgar Allen Poe, *The Gold Bug.* A vellum with a cryptogram inscribed on it was found. For convenience, we enumerate the characters of the cryptogram in the order they were written (see Figure 2). In

1	2	3	4	5	6	7	8	9	10	11	12	13	14	15	16	17	18	19
5	3	#	#	+	3	0	5	)	)	6	*	;	4	8	2	6	)	4

20	21	22	23	24	25	26	27	28	29	30	31	32	33	34	35	36
#	•	)	4	#	)	;	8	0	6	*	;	4	8	+	8	□

37	38	39	40	41	42	43	44	45	46	47	48	49	50	51	52
6	0	)	)	8	5	;	;	]	8	*	;	:	#	*	8

53	54	55	56	57	58	59	60	61	62	63	64	65	66	67	68	69
+	8	3	(	8	8	)	5	*	+	;	4	6	(	;	8	8

70	71	72	73	74	75	76	77	78	79	80	81	82	83	84	85	86
*	9	6	*	?	;	8	)	*	#	(	;	4	8	5	)	;

87	88	89	90	91	92	93	94	95	96	97	98	99	100	101	102
5	*	+	2	:	*	#	(	;	4	9	5	6	*	2	(

103	104	105	106	107	108	109	110	111	112	113	114	115
5	*	=	4	)	8	□	8	*	;	4	0	6

116	117	118	119	120	121	122	123	124	125	126	127	128
9	2	8	5	)	;	)	6	+	8	)	4	#

129	130	131	132	133	134	135	136	137	138	139	140	141	142
#	;	1	(	#	9	;	4	8	0	8	1	;	8

143	144	145	146	147	148	149	150	151	152	153	154	155	156
:	8	#	1	;	4	8	+	8	5	;	4	)	4

157	158	159	160	161	162	163	164	165	166	167	168	169
8	5	+	5	2	8	8	0	6	*	8	1	(

170	171	172	173	174	175	176	177	178	179	180	181	182
#	9	;	4	8	;	(	8	8	;	4	(	#

183	184	185	186	187	188	189	190	191	192	193	194	195
?	3	4	;	4	8	)	4	#	;	1	6	1

196	197	198	199	200	201	202	203	204
;	:	1	8	8	;	#	?	;

Figure 2

addition to the characters, a skull and a kid were depicted on the vellum. The main character heard of one Captain Kidd and his buried treasures. The kid on the vellum was situated beneath the text of characters and was, therefore, definitely a kind of punning signature. The pun upon the word "Kidd" makes sense in no other language but English. Thus there were all the reasons to assume that the language of the cipher was English. Moreover, Captain Kidd was not that much of an intellectual to use any complicated and hard to break cipher; hence, most probably, a simple substitution cipher was used. There are no divisions between words; had there been divisions, the task would have been much easier because the analysis of the shorter words would have readily reveal the ciphertext equivalents for I, A, THE, etc. Anyway, having no divisions, the first step was to count the number of times each character occurs in the cryptogram

$$8 \quad ; \quad 4 \quad) \quad \# \quad * \quad 5 \quad 6 \quad (\quad + \quad 1 \quad 0 \quad 2 \quad 9 \quad : \quad 3 \quad ? \quad \Box \quad \bullet \quad] \quad =$$
$$34 \quad 27 \quad 19 \quad 16 \quad 15 \quad 14 \quad 12 \quad 11 \quad 9 \quad 8 \quad 7 \quad 6 \quad 5 \quad 5 \quad 4 \quad 4 \quad 3 \quad 2 \quad 1 \quad 1 \quad 1$$

In English, the letter that occurs most frequently is e. Afterwards, the succession runs as: a, o, i, d, h, n, r, s, t, u, y, c, f, g, l, m, w, b, k, j, p, q, x, z. The letter e predominates so remarkably that in almost any sentence it is a prevailing character. These observations provided some groundwork to proceed with further analysis. The count of frequencies is always very useful, and in our case it is employed in the initial stage of the analysis. Since *8* is the prevailing character, it was assumed to be e. In support of this, note that the combination *88* appears five times, and in English, the letter e is doubled more frequently than other letters.

Of all English words, "the" is most frequent. Thus it is reasonable to look for repetitions of any three characters, in the same order, the last of them being *8*. Upon careful inspection, it can be seen that these characters are *;48*. Therefore, it can be assumed that *;* is t, *4* represents h and *8* is actually e. Thus a great step has been taken.

Having established a single word, it is possible to establish commencements and terminations of other words. Consider *;48* at positions 172, 173, and 174. Hence *;* at position 175 is the first letter of a word. Of the six characters succeeding this "the" we know five. Replacing the characters by the letters and putting a dot for the unknown character, we get "t.eeth". There are no English words of this type starting with "t" and containing "th". This can be checked by substitution of the alphabet for the dot. Rejecting "th" and trying successively each letter of the alphabet as the unknown letter in "t.ee", we see that the omitted letter is "r". Thus the value of *(* is r. We know two successive words "the tree".

Looking beyond these words, we see again the combination *;48* (positions 186–188). In this case, it may indicate the termination of a word. We get the arrangement

the tree ;4(#?34 the

Substituting the letters where known and replacing the unknown characters by dots, we get

the tree thr...h the

Here the word "through" becomes evident at once. Thus we know that *#*, *?*, and *3* represent o, u, and g, respectively.

Looking through the cipher for combinations of known characters we find, not very far from the beginning, the group *83(88* (positions 54–58). This reads "egree" and, clearly, is the conclusion of the word "degree". The value of *+* is d. Four letters after the word "degree", we see *;46(;88**. As before, translating the known characters and representing the unknown by dots, we get th.rtee, an arrangement suggestive for the word "thirteen". This gives us letters i and n, represented by *6* and ***.

The cryptogram starts with the combination *53##+*. Substituting, as before, we obtain .good, which assures us that the first letter is a. The first two words are "A good". Thus, the following is discovered

5	+	8	3	4	6	*	#	(	;	?
a	d	e	g	h	i	n	o	r	t	u

At this point, E. Poe terminates his analysis. Now we will reconstruct some lacking details. The value of the symbol *)* is unknown, though this symbol is of the fourth greatest frequency because it appears 16 times in the cryptogram. At the same time, we still do not know what symbol represents the letter s, which is in the top ten of the most frequently occurring letters. Therefore, at first sight, *)* must be s. This hypothesis is partially supported by the fact that *)* is not a vowel, since otherwise senseless combinations of letters result,

6	7	8	9	10	11	12
g	.	a	)	)	i	n

or

37	38	39	40	41	42
i	.	)	)	e	a

Another confirmation that) is s is provided by the segment of the cryptogram (positions 60–89) ".and thirteen .inutes north east and". Thus) is s, and *9* is m.

Substituting consecutively letters of the alphabet for the character *0* (positions 7 and 28) we see that its only possible value is l.

It follows from the analysis of the segment 107–113 that □ is v.

The segment 22–70 contains only two uncovered characters, namely,] and :. In this segment, these characters appear just once. Obviously,] is w and : is y. The part of the cryptogram 172–204 contains only one character, *1*, whose value is unknown. It can be easily noted that this value is f.

The character *2* at positions 117 and 90 is evidently the encryption of b.

Now all we have to do is to guess the values of • and =. Trying the remaining letters we find that = is c, and the value of • is one of the following: k, p, q, x, z. The only possible termination of the word bisho. (positions 17–21) is p.

Thus all the 21 characters from the cryptogram are determined. The cryptogram reads: "A good glass in the bishop's hostel in the devil's seat twenty one degrees and thirteen minutes northeast and by north main branch seventh limb east side shoot from the left eye of the death's head a bee line from the tree through the shot fifty feet out."

The cipher alphabet is as follows:

A	B	C	D	E	F	G	H	I	L	M	N	O	P	R	S	T	U	V	W	Y
5	2	=	+	8	1	3	4	6	0	9	*	#	•	(	)	;	?	□	]	:

J. Verne, *Journey to the Centre of the Earth.* Professor Lindenbrock came across a parchment with the cryptogram shown in Figure 3.

"It is Runic! These marks are exactly like those in the manuscript of Snorre Turleson. But what can they mean?", the professor

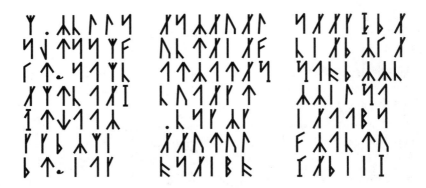

Figure 3

asked. "Yet it is the ancient Icelandic!" he muttered to himself. Upon inspection of the parchment, Lindenbrock concluded that those characters actually made up a secret message. First, he replaced each character of the cryptogram with the corresponding letter of the German alphabet of those days. "Now, then, I am going to dictate to you each letter of our alphabet which corresponds to one of these Icelandic characters," the professor said to his assistant. The following incomprehensible succession of words resulted

```
m . r n l l s       e s r e u e l       s e e c J d e
s g t s s m f       u n t e i e f       n i e d r k e
k t , s a m n       a t r a t e S       S a o d r r n
e m t n a e I       n u a e c t         r r i l S a
A t v a a r         . n s c r c         i e a a b s
c c d r m i         e e u t u l         f r a n t u
d t , i a c         o s e i b o         K e d i i I
```

Then Lindenbrock assumed that the cryptogram had been written by one of the former owners of the book between pages of which the parchment had been found. On the second page he found a spot, which looked like a blot of ink. With a magnifying glass, on closer inspection, the professor noticed half obliterated letters . That was translated as "Arne

Saknussem", a celebrated alchemist who lived in the sixteenth century.

After that, Lindenbrock's reasoning was as follows. "In this document there are 132 letters, out of which 79 are consonants and 53 vowels. Now this is just about the proportion found in the words of southern languages, while the northern idioms are far richer in consonants. Consequently this must be in a southern language." "This Saknussem," he went on, "was a learned man, and since he did not write in his mother tongue, he would be sure to employ the language in common use among the cultivated minds of the sixteenth century; I mean the Latin. If I am mistaken, I could try the Spanish, the French, the Italian, the Greek, the Hebrew. But the learned in the sixteenth century generally wrote in Latin. I may rightly, then, say, a priori — this is in Latin."

"Look at it thoroughly," he said, "Here are 132 letters in evident disorder. In some words there are nothing but consonants, as in the first, m.rnlls; others where the vowels, on the contrary, abound — the fifth, for example, unteief, or the last but one, oseibo. Now this arrangement has, clearly, not been designed. It is the mathematical result of the unknown law which ruled the succession of these letters. It seems to me certain that the primitive phrase has been written regularly, and then turned upside down, according to some law I must find out. Any one who had the key of the cipher could read it fluently. But where is the key?"

"It seems to me," said the professor, "that if one wished to mix up and confuse any sentence, the first thing he would think of would be to write the words vertically instead of horizontally." To verify that assumption he dictated to his assistant the letters, naming successively the first of each word, and then the second, and so on. The letters were arranged as follows:

```
messunkaSenrA.icefdoK.segnittamurtnece
rtserrette,rotaivsadua,ednecsedsadnelak
artniiiluJsiratracSarbmutabiledmekmeret
arcsilucoIsleffenSnI
```

But long after that, the professor could not advance further. He nearly fell into blank despair. "I involuntarily began to fan myself with the sheet of paper. The back and front of it alternately met my eye, and as it waved rapidly to and fro I fancied I could see on the back some perfectly legible Latin words, `craterem`, `terrestre`." The obtained sequence of letters was to be read in the opposite direction, from right to left. Just an accident revealed the clue to the problem! The deciphered cryptogram looks as follows:

"*In Sneffels Ioculis craterem kem delibat umbra Scartaris Julii intra calendas descende, audas viator, et terrestre centrum attinges. Kod feci. Arne Saknussem.*"

In English it reads

"*Descend the crater of the Jocul of Sneffel, that the shadow of Scartaris softly touches before the Kalends of July, bold traveller, and thou wilt reach the centre of the earth. Which I have done. Arne Saknussem.*"

3. Transposition ciphers

A cipher that only permutes the letters in a plaintext but does not change the letters themselves is called *a transposition cipher*.

Consider a transposition cipher suitable for enciphering messages of n letters long. It can be represented as follows:

$$(6) \qquad \begin{pmatrix} 1 & 2 & \ldots & n \\ i_1 & i_2 & \ldots & i_n \end{pmatrix}.$$

Here i_1 is the position in the ciphertext to which the first letter of the plaintext is to be moved, i_2 specifies the new position of the second letter of the message, etc. The first row in (6) represents the integers $1, 2, \ldots, n$ in the natural order; in the second row, the same integers are written out but in a different order. These two rows together constitute *a permutation of degree n*.

Suppose we are given the permutation associated to a transposition cipher; then we can easily perform both decryption and encryption. Let us do an example. The permutation

$$\begin{pmatrix} 1 & 2 & 3 & 4 & 5 & 6 \\ 5 & 2 & 3 & 1 & 4 & 6 \end{pmatrix}$$

ciphers WRITER to TRIEWR. Use this permutation to decipher НЧЕИУК.[1]

As an exercise, write out the permutations engaged in the three examples of transposition ciphers discussed below. The answers can be found at the end of this section.

The reader familiar with the mathematical induction can prove that the number of ways to fill the second row in (6) is $1 \cdot 2 \cdot 3 \cdots n$; the latter is usually denoted by $n!$ and called the factorial of n. Hence the number of different transposition ciphers available for an n-letter text (including the cipher that does not rearrange letters at all) is $n!$.

As n increases, $n!$ grows extremely rapidly. The values of $n!$ for the first ten positive integers are as follows:

n	1	2	3	4	5	6	7	8	9	10
$n!$	1	2	6	24	120	720	5040	40320	362880	3628800

For large n, Stirling's asymptotic formula yields

$$n! \approx \sqrt{2\pi n}\left(\frac{n}{e}\right)^n,$$

where $e = 2.718281828\ldots$.

Thus a transposition cipher for encrypting n-letter messages that works as shown above has $n!$ keys.

A random permutation, especially for large n, is usually hard to remember. For this reason, in practice the rearrangement of the letters of a plaintext is done with the aid of some type of geometric figure. The plaintext is written into the figure according to some "write-in" path. The ciphertext is taken off the figure according to some "take-off" path. Such a cipher is often spoken of as a *route transposition*. Consider an example. Let the figure be a rectangle divided into square cells. The "write-in" path can be as follows. We write the text from left to right into the first row, then from right to left into the second row, and so on (by alternate horizontals). The ciphertext is to be read off by columns; we take out the letters of the first column from top to bottom, the letters of the second column from bottom to top, etc. (by alternate verticals). To illustrate that,

---

[1]The answer is УЧЕНИК, which is the Russian for STUDENT.

let us encipher

HEHASTRAVELLEDALONEMANYTIMES

using a 4 × 7 array. We have

H	E	H	A	S	T	R
D	E	L	L	E	V	A
A	L	O	N	E	M	A
S	E	M	I	T	Y	N

The ciphertext reads

RAANYMVTSEETINLAHLOMELEEHDAS

Theoretically, paths for writing in and taking off can be far more complicated. At the same time, the use of peculiar paths seriously slows down both the decryption and the encryption.

Below we describe some kinds of transposition ciphers encountered in Olympiad problems.

Scytale cipher. The *scytale* is believed to be the oldest known concealment device. The Spartans used it during the wars against Athens in the fifth century B.C. The scytale was a rod around which a strip was wound slantwise. A message was written lengthwise of the rod. The strip was unrolled then and sent to the receiver who possessed a rod of exactly the same diameter and thus was able to read the message. It is clear that the scytale method changed the order of letters in a message.

For a message of n letters long, only n permutations of its letters can be realized by means of scytale ciphers. This follows from the solution of Problem 2.1. Indeed, a scytale cipher works exactly as the following route transposition: the letters of a message are written in by rows into an array with m columns ($m \leq n$); then the letters are read off by verticals.

Besides purely mathematical restrictions, there are also restrictions of physical nature that further reduce the number of permu-

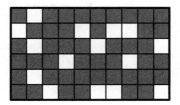

Figure 4

tations scytale ciphers provide. In practice, the diameter of the rod hardly exceeds 10 cm. Assuming the height of letters to be 1 cm, we see that one turn of the strip contains at most 32 letters (since $10\pi < 32$). Thus the number of permutations is not greater than 32.

Turning Grille. A grille can be prepared of a rectangular sheet of paper by dividing it into square cells ($2m$ rows and $2k$ columns) and clipping out mk cells to make apertures for writing letters in. The grille is placed on a sheet of paper of exactly the same size as the grille and divided into cells that correspond to those of the grille. The letters of a message are written into apertures by straight horizontals. Then the grille is rotated through 180° (or turned upside-down) into a new position on the same sheet of paper so as to expose other blank cells for writing letters. After the grille has taken all its four possible positions, each cell on the sheet of paper must be covered by an aperture exactly once.

Consider an example. A 6×10 grille is shown in Figure 4. The message to encrypt is

IAMADRIFTERONAHUNGRYANDEMPTYSEA

THEREISNOONEONEARTHTORESCUEME

After placing the grille on a sheet of paper, we write in the first 15 letters (that many apertures the grille has) IAMADRIFTERONAH ... . The text on the paper now looks as shown in Figure 5(a). Rotating the grille by 180° we get 15 blank cells. After writing the letters, the paper looks as indicated in Figure 5(b). Then we turn the grille upside down

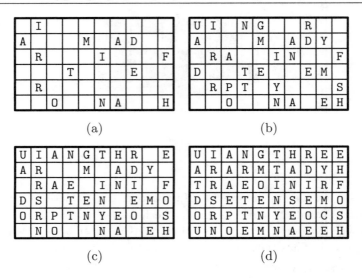

(a)   (b)

(c)   (d)

Figure 5

and write in the remaining letters in two steps (Figures 5(c), 5(d)). Using an exactly the same grille one can easily decrypt the message.

The number of ways to clip out the cells is $T = 4^{mk}$ (see Problem 1.1). This is the number of keys for this sort of ciphers. The cipher can be used to encrypt messages of $4mk$ letters. The number of all possible permutations of letters of such a message is $(4mk)!$, which is many times greater than T. However, even for a 8×8 grille the number of keys exceeds four billions, a very large number indeed.

Another example of a route transposition cipher is the so-called *columnar transposition cipher*. In this sort of ciphers, a message is written in rows from left to right into cells of a rectangular table. To make a ciphertext, the letters then are read off by columns. The order in which the columns are taken for reading off is the key of the cipher. For example, let the key be $(5, 4, 1, 7, 2, 6, 3)$. To encrypt the message

THEREISANEXAMPLEOFCOLUMNARTRANSPOSITIONCIPHER

we write it into a matrix whose columns are enumerated according to the key. We have

5	1	4	7	2	6	3
T	H	E	R	E	I	S
A	N	E	X	A	M	P
L	E	O	F	C	O	L
U	M	N	A	R	T	R
A	N	S	P	O	S	I
T	I	O	N	C	I	P
H	E	R	-	-	-	-

Taking the columns in the specified order and reading off (from top to bottom) the letters of each column, we arrive at

HNEMNIEEACROC-SPLRIP-EEONSORTALUATHIMOTSI-RXFAPN-

If the matrix for writing letters in has m columns, then the number of keys is $m!$. It is customary that m is much less than the length of the message n and, therefore, $m!$ is very small as compared with $n!$.

Suppose m divides n. Using Stirling's formula given above, try to estimate the ratio of $m!$ to the total number of permutations of letters for a text of length n.

To memorize a key, it is useful to associate it with a keyword whose letters represent numbers. For example, suppose the keyword is PERMUTATION. Let A represent 1. Since the letters B, C, D are not in the word, the nearest neighbor to A in the alphabet is E. We assign 2 to E. Then I is 3. If a letter appears more than once, the letter T in our case, all the occurrences of the letter are enumerated from left to right. Thus, T that is after U becomes 9, and T that is after A becomes 10. Finally, we get

P	E	R	M	U	T	A	T	I	O	N
7	2	8	4	11	9	1	10	3	6	5

Consider some issues related to breaking transposition ciphers. As noted above, the number of possible keys is large even for a short message. However, this is not the only difficulty. After trying each possible key, it can be hard to decide which of the results is the genuine plaintext. Indeed, what does the ciphertext ASLT mean? It could be SALT, LAST, or an abbreviation for the Soviet Agency of Lunar Tourism, or whichever. The ciphertext

INLIGUOHNTTMSIOYTOJS

can equally likely be either TOMISGUILTYJOHNISNOT or JOHN ISGUILTYTOMISNOT, the messages with exactly opposite meanings. Considering nothing but the ciphertext we cannot determine which is the actual plaintext.

Knowing some general characteristics of the device used for encryption we can get an idea of the type of transformation (permutation) the device performs. The *scytale cipher* in Problem 2.1 is a good example. As shown above, at most 32 permutations of the letters of a plaintext can be realized by this sort of ciphers. Due to that small number of keys, the exhaustive key search is possible. By doing so, if a ciphertext is long enough, a meaningful text is certain to appear just once. However, in Problem 2.1 the decryption can be done even faster because the cipherer inscribed spacing marks in some line. Thanks to the marks, it is easy to find the diameter of the rod (scytale) and, therefore, to determine the permutation of the letters of the plaintext.

Another example of such a "trapdoor" resulted from an improper use of an enciphering device is considered in Problem 4.1. Suppose we encrypt a message of $mr - k$ letters with an $m \times r$ grille. If $k \leq mr/4$, then the k unfilled cells correspond to the positions of the k apertures in the last placement of the grille. This remark seriously reduces the number of permissible grilles to $4^{mr/4-k}$. What is the number of permissible grilles for $k > mr/4$?

Answers to the Exercises

(1) Route transposition cipher:

1	2	3	4	5	6	7	8	9	10	11	12	13	14
25	24	17	16	9	8	1	2	7	10	15	18	23	26

15	16	17	18	19	20	21	22	23	24	25	26	27	28
27	22	19	14	11	6	3	4	5	12	13	20	21	28

(2) Turning grille:

1	2	3	4	5	6	7	8	9	10	11	12	13	14	15
2	11	15	17	18	22	26	30	34	38	42	53	56	57	60

16	17	18	19	20	21	22	23	24	25	26	27	28	29	30
1	4	5	8	19	23	27	31	35	39	43	44	46	50	59

31	32	33	34	35	36	37	38	39	40	41	42	43	44	45
3	6	7	10	12	24	28	32	36	40	41	45	47	48	52

46	47	48	49	50	51	52	53	54	55	56	57	58	59	60
9	13	14	16	20	21	25	29	33	37	49	51	54	55	58

(3) Columnar transposition cipher:

1	2	3	4	5	6	7	8	9	10	11	12	13	14	15
23	1	17	34	7	29	12	24	2	18	35	8	30	13	25

16	17	18	19	20	21	22	23	24	25	26	27	28	29	30
3	19	36	9	31	14	26	4	20	37	10	32	15	27	5

31	32	33	34	35	36	37	38
21	38	11	33	16	28	6	22

4. Periodic polyalphabetic substitution ciphers

Consider the standard 26-letter alphabet

ABCDEFGHIJKLMNOPQRSTUVWXYZ

The letters of almost any language possess an intrinsic order (the
lexicographical order) thus forming the alphabet. Dealing with an alphabet, it is customary to represent each letter by its natural position
number in the alphabet. In the Latin alphabet we consider, A is 1
and X is 24. Thus we can unambiguously convert a message into a sequence of numbers and vice versa. For example, the numeric message
1 12 16 8 1 2 5 20 is ALPHABET.

We can "extend our alphabet infinitely" assuming that after Z there go A, B,..., Z, then again A, B, ..., etc. This can be illustrated by placing the letters around a circle as shown in Figure 6. We say that the position of A with respect to Z is 1, while the position of A with respect to B is 25. In general, the position of one letter with respect to another is the remainder of the division of the difference of their natural positions by the size of the alphabet.

Consider the general case. Let N_1 and N_2 be the natural positions of two letters in an alphabet. Denote by $D(N_1, N_2)$ the position of the first letter (N_1) with respect to the second one (N_2).

Let $r_m(N)$ represent the remainder of N when divided by m.

Then $D(N_1, N_2) = r_l(N_1 - N_2)$, where l is the size of the alphabet.

For convenience, we denote $N_1 \ominus N_2 = r_l(N_1 - N_2)$ and $N_1 \oplus N_2 = r_l(N_1 + N_2)$. We have

$$(7) \qquad\qquad D(N_1, N_2) = N_1 \ominus N_2,$$
$$(8) \qquad\qquad N_1 = N_2 \oplus D(N_1, N_2).$$

The last formula, which follows immediately from (7), can be thought of as an encryption rule that calculates, for a plaintext letter N_2, its ciphertext equivalent N_1. In this case, the number $D(N_1, N_2)$ is referred to as a *character of the enciphering key*.

To help the reader to understand better the notions just introduced we offer the following problems.

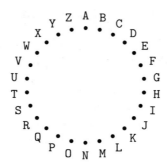

Figure 6

1. Prove that for arbitrary integers N_1 and N_2 and any positive integer l the following is true: $D(N_1, N_2) = N_1 - N_2 - \left[\frac{N_1 - N_2}{l}\right] \cdot l$, where $[X]$ denotes the integral part of X (the greatest integer less than or equal to X).

2. Prove equality (8) as well as the following equality:

$$(9) \qquad N_2 = N_1 \ominus D(N_1, N_2).$$

To encrypt an N-letter plaintext by means of the rule (8), we need an enciphering key sequence of N characters: each letter of the plaintext is replaced with the corresponding key character.

However, a key does not always have to be as long as the plaintext itself. With a short key (a keyword), we can break the plaintext into groups of size equal to the length of the key and then encrypt each group successively. Such a cipher is called a *periodic substitution cipher.*

The number of T-letter words in an l-letter alphabet is l^T. Indeed, for each of the T spaces there are l available characters. Below, some values of l^T for $l = 30$ are shown:

T	1	2	3	4	5	6
30^T	30	900	27000	810000	24300000	$0.729 \cdot 10^9$

T	7	8	9	10
30^T	$0.2187 \cdot 10^{11}$	$0.6561 \cdot 10^{12}$	$0.19683 \cdot 10^{14}$	$0.59049 \cdot 10^{15}$

It is thus clear that the number of keys grows rapidly with T; for $T = 10$ the exhaustive key search is practically infeasible.

With each character of a keyword we can associate a simple substitution, e.g., for the character 1 we have

```
ABCDEFGHIJKLMNOPQRSTUVWXYZ
BCDEFGHIJKLMNOPQRSTUVWXYZA
```

The second row is called a *cipher alphabet*; it is customary, when writing down a keyword, to replace each character with the first letter of a corresponding cipher alphabet. Thus, instead of 1 we shall write B. Suppose a keyword is T characters long; then letters of the plaintext that are $T - 1$ positions apart from each other are encrypted by using

```
A B C D E F G H I J K L M N O P Q R S T U V W X Y Z
B C D E F G H I J K L M N O P Q R S T U V W X Y Z A
C D E F G H I J K L M N O P Q R S T U V W X Y Z A B
D E F G H I J K L M N O P Q R S T U V W X Y Z A B C
E F G H I J K L M N O P Q R S T U V W X Y Z A B C D
F G H I J K L M N O P Q R S T U V W X Y Z A B C D E
G H I J K L M N O P Q R S T U V W X Y Z A B C D E F
H I J K L M N O P Q R S T U V W X Y Z A B C D E F G
I J K L M N O P Q R S T U V W X Y Z A B C D E F G H
J K L M N O P Q R S T U V W X Y Z A B C D E F G H I
K L M N O P Q R S T U V W X Y Z A B C D E F G H I J
L M N O P Q R S T U V W X Y Z A B C D E F G H I J K
M N O P Q R S T U V W X Y Z A B C D E F G H I J K L
N O P Q R S T U V W X Y Z A B C D E F G H I J K L M
O P Q R S T U V W X Y Z A B C D E F G H I J K L M N
P Q R S T U V W X Y Z A B C D E F G H I J K L M N O
Q R S T U V W X Y Z A B C D E F G H I J K L M N O P
R S T U V W X Y Z A B C D E F G H I J K L M N O P Q
S T U V W X Y Z A B C D E F G H I J K L M N O P Q R
T U V W X Y Z A B C D E F G H I J K L M N O P Q R S
U V W X Y Z A B C D E F G H I J K L M N O P Q R S T
V W X Y Z A B C D E F G H I J K L M N O P Q R S T U
W X Y Z A B C D E F G H I J K L M N O P Q R S T U V
X Y Z A B C D E F G H I J K L M N O P Q R S T U V W
Y Z A B C D E F G H I J K L M N O P Q R S T U V W X
Z A B C D E F G H I J K L M N O P Q R S T U V W X Y
```

Figure 7

the same simple substitution. Since there are 26 available characters $(0, 1, 2, \ldots, 25)$, we have 26 simple substitutions (see Figure 7). These shifted alphabets are known as Vigenère Tableau, called so after the French cryptologist Blaise de Vigenère. The Tableau was given in his *Treatise on Ciphers* published in 1585.

The Vigenère Tableau facilitates encryption and decryption. For a plaintext letter x_1 and a key letter x_2, the ciphertext is the letter in the column x_1 of the row x_2. For a ciphertext letter z and a key letter x_2, the plaintext letter is the column containing z in the row x_2. For example, for the ciphertext letter m and the key letter h, the corresponding plaintext letter is f.

Consider now how the Vigenère Cipher could be cryptanalyzed. The first step is to determine the keyword length m. This can be done by the so-called *Kasiski test* or using the concept of the *index of coincidence*.

The Kasiski test was first described by Friedrich Kasiski in 1863. It is based on the observation that two identical segments of a plaintext yield the same ciphertext whenever their occurrence in the plaintext is m positions apart. Conversely, if we observe two identical segments of a ciphertext, each of length at least three, say, then there is a good chance that they do correspond to identical segments of the plaintext. The Kasiski test works as follows. We search the ciphertext for pairs of identical segments of length at least three, and record the distance between the starting positions of corresponding segments. If we obtain several such distances $d_1, d_2, \ldots, d_n$, then it is reasonable to assume that m divides the greatest common divisor of the d_i's. Usually, one of these divisors is the key length.

To confirm this guess, one can use the *index of coincidence* introduced by Wolfe Friedman in 1920. Consider a string y of a ciphertext, say $y = \texttt{GERCIEYUG}$. The string is 9 letters long. The number of ways to choose two letters from y is $\binom{9}{2} = 36$. The number of pairs of identical letters in y (these are $\texttt{GG}$ and $\texttt{EE}$) is 2. The index of coincidence for y is $2/36 \approx 0.055$. A more mathematically inclined reader may realize that the index of coincidence for a string is the probability that two random characters of the string are equal. For a random string of English letters the index is approximately 0.038, while for an average meaningful English text it makes about 0.065. It is important to note (though this is absolutely clear), that the index of coincidence cannot be affected by a simple substitution.

Now, suppose we have a ciphertext of length n obtained by using the Vigenère Cipher. Our task is to check if m is likely to be the keyword length. We write out the text, by columns, in a rectangular $m \times (n/m)$-array. If m is indeed the keyword length, then for each row the index of coincidence should be roughly equal to 0.065.

To illustrate the Kasiski test and the use of the index of coincidence, consider the following example. The following ciphertext is obtained from the Vigenère Cipher:

```
CHREEVOAHMAERATBIAXXWTNXBEEOPHBSBQMQEQERBW
RVXUOAKXAOSXXWEAHBWGJMMQMNKGRFVGXWTRZXWIAK
LXFPSKAUTEMNDCMGTSXMXBTUIADNGMGPSRELXNJELX
VRVPRTULHDNQWTWDTYGBPHXTFALJHASVBFXNGLLCHR
ZBWELEKMSJIKNBHWRJGNMGJSGLXFEYPHAGNRBIEQJT
AMRVLCRREMNDGLXRRIMGNSNRWCHRQHAEYEVTAQEBBI
PEEWEVKAKOEWADREMXMTBHHCHRTKDNVRZCHRCLQOHP
WQAIIWXNRMGWOIIFKEE
```

First, let us try the Kasiski test. The ciphertext string CHR occurs at four places in the ciphertext, beginning at positions 1, 166, 236 and 286. The distances from the first occurrence to the other three occurrences are (respectively) 165, 235, and 285. The greatest common divisor of these three integers is 5, so that is very likely the keyword length. Let us see if the computation of indices of coincidence leads to the same conclusion. With $m = 1$, the index of coincidence is 0.045. With $m = 2$, the two indices are 0.046 and 0.041. With $m = 3$, we get 0.043, 0.050, and 0.047. With $m = 4$, we have the indices 0.042, 0.039, 0.046, and 0.040. Then trying $m = 5$ we obtain the values 0.063, 0.068, 0.069, 0.061, and 0.072. This also provides strong evidence that the keyword length is five.

Having determined the key length, we can proceed by merely trying all five-letter words. With modern computers, which are able to tell an intelligible English text from a random sequence of letters, it will not take long since we have only 5^{26} keywords to check. Besides, the sought keyword is most likely to be an actual English word, not just a random combination. If this is indeed the case, the amount of computation reduces dramatically.

In this example the keyword is JANET, and the complete decryption looks as follows:

The almond tree was in tentative blossom. The days were longer, often ending with magnificent evenings of corrugated pink skies. The hunting season was over, with hounds and guns put away for six months. The vineyards were busy again as the well-organized farmers treated their vines and the more lackadaisical neighbors hurried to do the pruning they should have done in November. (P. Mayle, *A Year in Provence*, A. Knopf, Inc., 1989.)

Other ideas concerned with the cryptanalysis of polyalphabetic ciphers can be found in the solutions of Problems 1.2, 2.2, 2.5, 3.4, 3.5, and 4.6.

5. Problems

Below we present problems offered at the Olympiads on Cryptography and Mathematics for high school students. None of the problems require anything beyond the standard high school curriculum. Some problems are quite easy, whereas others require difficult and long analysis. However, each problem we present was solved by at least one participant of the Olympiad. In some problems, the original cryptograms were replaced by English versions. However, we have not replaced those Russian cryptograms that can be solved with no (or very little) knowledge of the Russian.[2]

1.1   Consider the cipher called *a turning grille*. Suppose we have a square sheet of paper marked into cells such that there are $2n$ rows and $2n$ columns (n is an integer). Some cells (namely, n^2 of them) are clipped out to make apertures for writing letters. One edge of the grille is marked. On another sheet of paper, there is a $2n \times 2n$ blank table of exactly the same size as the grille. We can place the grille on the table in four ways, namely, aligning the marked edge with each of the four borders of the table. The apertures are selected in such a way that each aperture opens its own four cells on the paper, causing each of them to be opened exactly once.

A plaintext of length $4n^2$ letters is written into the cells of the table in the following way. First, the grille covers the table so that the marked edge coincides with the table's upper border. We write the letters through each aperture until all are filled. Then we turn

---

[2]EDITORIAL NOTE: The numbering of the problems has to do with the Olympiads at which they were offered.

the grille through $90°$, write the letters in, etc. The table filled with the letters of the plaintext is our cryptogram.

Find the number of possible keys for every n.

1.2   The following cryptogram has been received:

ECGUCTUJKHV

The encryption algorithm is as follows. Let x_1, x_2 be the roots of the polynomial $x^2 + 3x + 1$. Each letter of the plaintext is replaced with its position number in the English alphabet (A is 1 and Z is 26). Then, to every number the value of the polynomial $f(x) = x^6 + 3x^5 + x^4 + x^3 + 4x^2 + 4x + 3$ either at x_1 or at x_2 is added. After that, the numbers obtained are replaced with letters. Recover the plaintext.

1.3   Harrivace, the fixed-post spy in Nagonia, uses the following procedure to transmit messages to a recently planted undercover agent.

All the messages Harrivace can send are numbered $1, 2, 3, \ldots$. Having an excellent memory, the agent remembers the contents and the number of every message. Therefore, Harrivace sends to the agent only the number of a message, not the message itself.

A number is transmitted by leaving an amount of cash equal to this number at a predetermined place.

At the time the agent was planted, one, three, seven and 10 boot bank notes were in circulation in Nagonia (*boot* is the official monetary unit of Nagonia). But then, due to inflation and a monetary reform, one and three boot bank notes were withdrawn from circulation.

Find the least integer n such that any message with number greater than or equal to n can be transmitted by using the current bank notes.

1.4   Find all ordered pairs of positive integers (a, b) such that their greatest common divisor, d, is 6 and the least common multiple, m, is 6930. By factoring m and d into primes, solve the problem for arbitrary m and d.

1.5 In the cryptogram

$$
\begin{array}{ccccc}
\text{CO} & \times & \text{N} & = & \text{CPC} \\
+ & & \times & & - \\
\text{II} & + & \text{I} & = & \text{OY} \\
= & & = & & = \\
\text{EDP} & + & \text{TR} & = & \text{ETO}
\end{array}
$$

replace each letter with a digit in such a way that the specified equalities hold. Note that different digits correspond to different letters. To obtain the plaintext, write the letters in increasing order of the digits corresponding to them.

1.6 A company has offered a device that checks passwords for validity. A password is an ordered sequence of letters from the three letter alphabet $\{a, b, c\}$. Denote such sequences by capital letters. The device transforms the password to be checked, P, into a sequence Q according to the rule $Q = \varphi(P)$. Although the transformation φ is secret, some of its features have become public. First, there are sequences it cannot be applied to. For a sequence P the device can deal with, we have

1) $\varphi(aP) = P$;

2) $\varphi(bP) = \varphi(P)a\varphi(P)$;

3) the sequence $\varphi(cP)$ is the sequence $\varphi(P)$ written in the reverse order.

The device accepts a password P as valid if $\varphi(P) = P$. For example, bab is a valid password because $\varphi(bab) = \varphi(ab)a\varphi(ab) = bab$. Find a valid password of length more than three.

2.1 An ancient cipher called *scytale* was a rod around which a narrow strip of parchment was carefully wound with edges meeting uniformly at all points. The message to be communicated had been written lengthwise of the rod, then, the strip was unrolled and sent to the receiver. Having an exact copy the same rod, the receiver was able to decrypt the message.

We have received a message encrypted by a scytale cipher. Fortunately, the sender, careful to write the text in nonoverlapping rows, drew parallel lines along the rod. Hence, after having the strip unrolled, some groups of letters turned out to be separated from each other by dashes. Every dash makes an angle α with the edge of the strip, the width of the strip is d and the dash-to-dash distance is h. Knowing these parameters, how can one recover the message?

2.2   A plaintext is a sequence of digits. For encryption, it is divided successively into groups of five digits. Treating a group as a five-digit integer, we find, for every pair of neighboring groups, the sum of the corresponding integers and write the last two digits of the result immediately after the pair. Then, to every digit of the resulting sequence the term with the same number of an integer-valued arithmetic progression is added and the result is reduced modulo 10.

Solve the cryptogram

$$423461405313$$

2.3   Each digit x of a plaintext is replaced with the remainder of the division of $F(x) = b\left(x^3 + 7x^2 + 3x + a\right)$ by 10 (a, b are fixed positive integers).

Find all pairs a, b such that this transformation has a unique inverse and, therefore, is a valid encrypting transformation.

2.4   The keyboard of a combination lock has 26 keys A, B, ..., Z. To each key a positive integer is assigned. The same integer may be associated to different keys. After some keys are pressed, the integers corresponding to them sum up. The lock opens provided the sum is divisible by 26.

Prove that whatever numbers are assigned to the keys, the lock can be opened.

2.5   For encryption of a message in English, a string of English letters of the same length as the original message is used. The letters of the English alphabet are numbered as follows: A is 1, B is 2, ... , Y is 25, Z is 0. The message and the string are first converted into a sequence of integers, then each integer of the message is added modulo 26 to the corresponding integer of the string. The results are replaced then by their alphabetical equivalents to give the ciphertext.

Two messages are encrypted by means of the same string. Each message contains the plural noun QUESTIONS. The encrypted messages read

WQUZJSUNJETIXNIBNGQB

IXKZVMABJQTFVJHMQWIC

Reconstruct the messages.

2.6 The letters of the English alphabet are numbered as shown:

A	B	C	D	E	F	G	H	I	J	K	L	M	N	O	P	Q	R	S	T	U	V	W	X	Y	Z
1	2	3	4	5	6	7	8	9	10	11	12	13	14	15	16	17	18	19	20	21	22	23	24	25	0

A message of n letters is encrypted by using a key sequence of n letters. The encryption is as follows. The number of each letter of the message is added to the number of the corresponding letter of the sequence, the result is reduced modulo 26 and replaced with the letter from the table.

Suppose that the key sequence contains no other letters but K, E, and Y. Decipher the ciphertext SFUJLYNNPSTKTCFX.

3.1 A simple substitution cipher replaces each plaintext letter with a corresponding ciphertext letter. Different plaintext letters cannot be replaced with the same ciphertext letter. The key of a simple substitution cipher is a table that establishes the correspondence between ciphertext letters and plaintext letters. The simple substitution cipher with the key

A B C D E F G H I J K L M N O P Q R S T U V W X Y Z
S N P U J C M G O V L Z W H K X F D A B R I T Q E Y

encrypts the word SECRET to the word AJPDJB. Encrypting the latter with this cipher, we get SVXUVN. Then we encrypt SVXUVN and so on. After repeating the encryption infinitely many times, how many different words will we finally get?

3.2 Before sending a message to Bob, Alice transforms it in the following way. First she encrypts it with a simple substitution cipher. Then she breaks the ciphertext into groups of 12 letters and transmits each group separately. The letters of a group can be numbered as $1, 2, \ldots, 12$. To Bob they are sent in the order $2, 4, 6, 8, 10, 12, 1, 3, 5, 7,$

9, 11. Having obtained the cryptogram, Bob encrypts it with another simple substitution cipher and in the same manner sends the result to Oscar. (The cipher alphabets used in the substitution ciphers, as well as the plaintext alphabet, are the standard English alphabet.) The cryptogram Oscar has received is as follows:

azybcxzdefwx

cxyyvgxzcfae

gasaxgieqswz

viibiwswvjde

One of the groups represents the word **CRYPTOGRAPHY** of the plaintext. Determine the plaintext.

3.3   Consider the sequence $C_1, C_2, \ldots, C_n, \ldots$, where C_n is the last digit in the decimal notation of the number n^n. Prove that the sequence is periodic with the smallest period 20.

3.4   A message is composed of Russian letters and the character – which indicates the space between words. The message is converted into a sequence of digits according to the table

А	Б	В	Г	Д	Е	Ж	З	И	К	Л	М	Н	О	П
01	02	03	04	05	06	07	08	09	10	11	12	13	14	15
Р	С	Т	У	Ф	Х	Ц	Ч	Ш	Щ	Ь	Ы	Э	Ю	Я	-
16	17	18	19	20	21	22	23	24	25	26	27	28	29	30	31

Then the numbers $C_k, C_{k+1}, \ldots$ described in Problem 3.3 are used. Let k be an arbitrary positive integer. We add C_k to the first digit of our sequence, then we add C_{k+1} to the second digit, etc. The result of each addition is replaced with its last digit. Decipher the cryptogram

23398672164581606706170617315588

3.5   An equilateral triangle ABC is divided into four parts as shown in Figure 8. Here M and N are the midpoints of the segments AB and BC, respectively; $PK \perp MQ$ and $NL \perp MQ$. The four parts can be put together to make up a square. Find $AP : PQ : QC$.

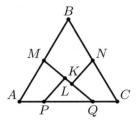

Figure 8

4.1 The key for *a turning grille cipher* is a rectangular stencil ruled as a 6 × 10 table. Some cells of the table are clipped out to make apertures for writing letters. The table with some cells cut is called a *grille*. There is a sheet of paper of the same size and shape as the grille and divided into cells that correspond to those of the grille. The grille can be placed on the sheet of paper in four ways. As the grille takes its four positions, each cell on the paper finds itself exactly one time beneath an aperture.

The letters of a message are written into apertures from left to right and from top to bottom. There are no intervals between words. Reconstruct the message if the ciphertext is

J	T	O	O	H	F	T	N	I	I
I	M	N	G	C	–	S	A	D	–
–	N	E	E	–	D	V	T	–	B
O	O	–	O	T	M	–	O	E	A
T	K	D	A	H	L	E	M	–	O
–	A	K	–	–	E	E	–	T	P

4.2 An encrypted passage from one of L. Carroll's verses looks like this:

15   23 2 20 3   7   1 2 23 23 7 22 2   3 11   3 18 2   10 15 23 18 :

15   3 11 26 21   3 18 2 1

"3 18 15 23   15 23   13 18 7 3   15   13 15 23 18."

3 18 2   26 15 3 3 26 2   10 15 23 18 2 23   11 10   3 18 2   23 2 7

3 18 2 8   23 2 20 3   7 20   20 7 23 13 2 19   14 7 16 9   3 11   1 2.

3 18 2   26 15 3 3 26 2   10 15 23 18 2 23   7 20 7 23 13 2 19   13 7 23

"13 2   16 7 20 20 11 3   21 11   15 3,   23 15 19,   14 2 16 7 12 23 2."

Each letter was replaced with an integer from 1 to 26; different letters were replaced with different integers. The punctuation was preserved. The letters are separated by spaces and the words by bigger spaces. Reconstruct the passage.

4.3   The *cipher disk* is used to encipher messages composed of numbers. It consists of two disks: a bigger one that is fixed and a smaller one which can rotate. The digits 0 to 9 are evenly spaced on the outer border of each disk. On encryption, a digit X on the bigger disk is ciphered into a digit Y on the smaller disk that lies on the same radius as X.

To be able to build such a device it is crucial to know how to inscribe a regular decagon into a circle or, what is the same, to know how to construct an angle of 36°. Using paper and pencil, find the value of any trigonometric function for 36° with accuracy 0.1.

4.4   Encryption of a sentence in Latin is performed in two steps. In the first step each letter of the sentence is replaced with the next to its right in the Latin alphabet (Z is replaced with A). In the second step, the text obtained is encrypted with a simple substitution cipher, namely, each letter of the text is replaced with another letter of the same alphabet (different letters are replaced with different letters). Moreover, this simple substitution is so chosen that, for an arbitrary plaintext, the ciphertext does not depend on the order in which the two steps are applied.

Read the encrypted Latin sentence

OSZJX FXRF YOQJSZ RAYFJ

Here each group of letters corresponds to one word of the phrase. The Latin alphabet (24 letters) is as follows:

A B C D E F G H I J L M N O P Q R S T U V X Y Z

4.6   Each letter of a message in Russian is replaced with a two-digit number:

А	Б	В	Г	Д	Е	Ж	З	И	К	Л	М	Н	О	П
00	01	02	03	04	05	06	07	08	09	10	11	12	13	14

Р	С	Т	У	Ф	Х	Ц	Ч	Ш	Щ	Ь	Ы	Э	Ю	Я
15	16	17	18	19	20	21	22	23	24	25	26	27	28	29

To encrypt the sequence of numbers corresponding to the message, one takes the sequence $A_1, A_2, \ldots$ defined by the rule $A_1 = 3$, $A_{k+1} = A_k + 3(k^2 + k + 1)$ ($k \in \mathbb{N}$) and applies it, starting with A_{100}. Namely, A_{100} is added to the first number of the message, A_{101} is added to the second number, etc. The result of each addition is reduced modulo 30 and the remainder is converted back into a letter. Find the message for the ciphertext КЕНЗЭРЕ.

4.7 The following mnemonics were offered to help memorize a periodically changing password. The password is the six leading digits of the smallest root of the equation

$$a(x^2 - 1) = \sqrt{1 + \frac{x}{a}}$$

written in decimal notation. Here a is a known quantity (say, the date). If the smallest root has less than six digits, then an appropriate number of zeros is added to the right of its last digit. Solve the equation for each $a > 0$.

5.1 The combination of a safe is a set of three integers x, y, z between 10 and 20 inclusive such that $F(x, y, z) = 99$. Find all possible combinations if

$$F(x, y, z) = 3x^2 - y^2 - 7z.$$

5.4 An English text was encrypted by substituting a pair of digits for each letter. Different letters were replaced with different pairs. Having intercepted the encrypted text, an enemy cryptanalyst tries to recover the text. In which case is he more likely to succeed: 1) he knows that the first word in the second line of the text is *assassinate* or 2) he knows that the first word in the third line of the text is *instance*? Explain your answer.

5.6   Each of the three ciphertexts

JPMIOUQSVZCAOBXWE

RMFHOBDSKOCGOLMWNO

FFMUVOYCSOPCVOAWKQ

was derived from the plaintext MOSCOW by using the same encryption algorithm. The following three cryptograms are obtained via the same algorithm:

1) WBXEAFTSTUEJLRNLBIAGKTVEWTTAEHLAENBINMTEJXVCELURSS;

2) NFEUIVRISWETMUTZHOIMNWTKOTCHQEEAXNDSJPHFEMARWKHI;

3) AZBMKEOTBETMEORSALCAUTHDEQMTSOHIAPPNENODEVVNOETRZ.

Two of them correspond to the same plaintext. The cryptograms are well-known sayings. What are these sayings?

6.1   In a communication network that includes 1997 users, each user is directly connected with exactly N other users. Find all possible values of N.

6.2   In each cell of a 1997 × 1997 table an integer from 1 to 1997 is inscribed in such a way that in each row of the table all the numbers from 1 to 1997 are present. The numbers located symmetrically with respect to the main diagonal are equal. (The main diagonal is that from the upper-left corner to the lower-right corner.) Find the sum of the numbers on the main diagonal.

6.3   The ciphertext

DEXITNDULSAUREEENTHS

SEACHANEELTYFIRSINDU

NTSTTENACSETANOLIDDI

TYNTEHDNIEE

was obtained by rearranging letters of the plaintext. The ciphertext

> ZXNFBNFCEGCFLNTTBFLG
>
> EBTGNTBWBNCVHBFSLFVC
>
> BHCZLNBLCGEKDGNTFSBV
>
> NGFFSBKNBBT

was obtained from the same plaintext by using a simple substitution (each letter of the plaintext was replaced with a corresponding letter of the ciphertext; this mapping is one-to-one). Reconstruct the plaintext.

6.4 There is a train of three gears, $1, 2$, and 3. Each gear is free to rotate around its own axis. Gear 1 is in mesh with gear 2, and gear 2 is in mesh with gear 3. Gear 1 has 33 teeth, gear 2 has 10 teeth, and gear 3 has 7 teeth. Each tooth of the first gear represents a letter of the Russian alphabet[3]

А Б В Г Д Е Ё Ж З И Й К Л М Н О П Р С Т У Ф Х Ц Ч Ш Щ Ъ Ы Ь Э Ю Я

The letters are inscribed on the teeth in the alphabetical order clockwise. The teeth of the second and third gears are numbered consecutively clockwise as $0, 1, 2, 3, 4, 5, 6, 7, 8, 9$ (gear 1) and $0, 1, 2, 3, 4, 5, 6$ (gear 2). On each axis an arm is fixed. While the arm of the first gear points at a letter, the other arms point at digits.

The letters of a message are encrypted successively. To encrypt a letter, we rotate gear 1 counterclockwise to set the arm at this letter, then we take out the digit pointed at on gear 2 and that on gear 3 thus forming an ordered pair. This pair is the ciphertext equivalent for the letter. Assume now that originally the arms point at A (gear 1), 0 (gear 2), 0 (gear 3). a) Encrypt the word ОЛИМПИАДА;[4] b) decrypt the ciphertext 24809283911211.

6.5 The digits $1, 2, \ldots, 9$ (in an unknown order) are placed along a circle. For encryption, each nonzero digit of a plaintext is replaced

---

[3]The standard Russian alphabet consists of 33 letters. However, in some problems we are using the reduced alphabet obtained by putting Ё=Е, Й=И, etc. Words usually remain recognizable.

[4]This is the Russian for OLYMPIAD.

with the digit next to it on the circle proceeding clockwise. For decryption, each nonzero digit of a ciphertext is replaced with the next counterclockwise. We assume that zero remains unchanged during both decryption and encryption. Suppose we have a plaintext and the corresponding ciphertext. What are minimal requirements the plaintext and the ciphertext should meet to allow us to recover the arrangement of the digits along the circle?

6.6   Consider a sequence $a_1, a_2, a_3, \ldots$ such that a_n is the residue of p^{n+2} modulo 24. Prove that for any prime p, this sequence is periodic with period 2.

7.1   Consider a wire network with 10 nodes. Suppose the following condition holds: loss of any two nodes does not bring down the entire network, i.e., any two active nodes remain connected (perhaps, via other active nodes). Find the least number of links between nodes necessary to satisfy these conditions.

7.2   In a computer network, passwords composed of digits are used. The encrypted passwords are stored on a hard disk. Each character of a password is independently encrypted in the following way. The first character is unchanged. Any other character, a_n, $n > 1$, is replaced with a digit b according to a rule of the form $b = f(a_n, a_{n-1})$. The transformation f is so chosen that a password can be deduced uniquely from its encrypted version.

A list of encrypted passwords is as follows:

424918878039, 4245133784397, 5393511,

428540012393, 4262271910365, 4252370031465, 4245133784735

This list includes, among others, the encrypted versions of the passwords

4208212275831, 4242592823026.

Recover other passwords if possible.

7.3   The cryptogram

PRROCQOYIYTEELRUGOYOLSMDNNEWAFEKAGSCEFRAAAIHOSMMETT

was obtained as follows. The message was broken successively into groups of r letters ($r < 51$). In each group, the letters were rearranged according to the following rule. A letter with position number x ($x = 1, 2, \ldots, r$) in a group was moved to the position $f(x) = ax \oplus b$ in this group of the cryptogram. Here a and b are positive integers; $ax \oplus b$ is either the residue of $ax \oplus b$ modulo r (if the residue is different from zero) or r (if the residue is zero). Find the plaintext.

7.4 In 1759, the great mathematician Leonard Euler described a *knight's closed tour* on the chessboard, which moves the knight over all 64 squares, visiting each square exactly once, and ending in the same square it started. By following the route of the knight, a text is written in the squares of the chessboard (see Figure 9). The text starts in a4. Read the text.

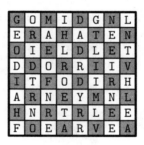

Figure 9

7.6 A piece of chalk is a rectangular parallelepiped of square cross-section with side length of 1 cm. When drawing with this chalk on a rectangular blackboard, the sides of the chalk cross-section must always remain parallel to the edges of the blackboard. Describe how to draw a convex polygon of area 1 square meter with the smallest possible area of the border. The area of the border does not contribute to the area of the polygon.

7.7 The digits $0, 1, \ldots, 9$ are split into disjoint groups. For each group, consider all the numbers containing, in decimal notation, every digit of the group exactly once. (The first digit can be 0.) All numbers thus obtained are arranged in the order of magnitude. To the kth number assign the kth letter of the alphabet

АБВГДЕЁЖЗИЙКЛМНОПРСТУФХЦЧШЩЪЫЬЭЮЯ

It turnes out that there is a one-to-one correspondence between the letters and the numbers. To encrypt a message, we replace each letter with the corresponding number. If the presentation of a number starts with 0, this 0 is not written out unless the number itself is zero. Solve the cryptogram 873146507381 and find numbers corresponding to all letters of the alphabet.

8.1   The logo of our Olympiad is shown in Figure 10.[5] It is a closed band folded in such a manner that the gaps (areas not covered by the band) are congruent regular triangles. Cutting the band at right angle to its edges and then unfolding it, we get a rectangle. Find the least possible ratio between the sides of the rectangle.

Figure 10

8.2   A message composed of zeros and ones can be encrypted in either of the following two ways. The first way is to replace each zero of the message with a sequence of k_1 zeros followed by k_2 ones, and each 1, with a sequence of k_3 zeros. In the second way, we replace each 1 with a sequence of k_4 ones followed by k_5 zeros, and each zero with a sequence of k_6 zeros. Find all 6-tuples of positive integers k_i, $i = 1, 2, \ldots, 6$, for which there exists at least one message such

---

[5]It says *"The 8th Olympiad on Cryptography and Mathematics, 1998"*.

that the ciphertexts obtained from the two algorithms are identical. Determine the general form of all such messages.

8.3 The message to be encrypted is a sequence of digits. This sequence represents the dates of birth of six members of the Olympiad Organizing Committee. Each date is a string of eight digits: the first two digits specify the day, the next two are for the month, and the other four are for the year. For instance, the brilliant mathematician L. Euler was born on April 4, 1707; his date of birth is represented as 04041707. To encrypt the message, we use a key sequence of 48 digits which is built in the following way. All odd prime numbers less than 100 are written consecutively in the order such that the difference between any two neighboring numbers is 2^n for some $n \in \mathbb{N}$. In this line each prime number must appear exactly once. The numbers 3, 5 and 7 are represented as $03, 05$, and 07. This string of primes consists of 48 digits and is taken as our key sequence.

To each digit of the message we add the corresponding digit of the key sequence and reduce the result modulo 10. The encrypted message reads

150220454213266744305682533362327363924975709849

Determine the six dates of birth.

8.4 A 13×13 square is divided into 169 small squares of size 1×1. Some squares are black, the remaining ones are white. Ciphy jumps from one square to another. As Ciphy jumps onto a square, all the squares situated at an integer distance from the square where Ciphy is now, change their color (from black to white and vice versa). (The distance from one square to another is the length of the segment connecting their centers.) After Ciphy has visited each square 1999 times, the big square looks as shown in Figure 11. Determine the original colors of the squares.

8.6 Factor $2^{30} + 1$ into primes.

9.1 Suppose we are given an n-letter alphabet $A_0, \dots, A_{n-1}$. We say that $A_k + A_l = A_m$ if the numbers $k + l$ and m yield the same remainder when divided by n. We can add up sequences of letters of

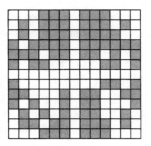

Figure 11

equal length simply by adding up the letters at corresponding places in two sequences. The result is a new sequence of the same length.

a) The Russian alphabet consists of 33 letters. Viewing it as a sequence of length 33, prove that there exists another sequence of 33 different letters of the Russian alphabet such that in the sum (in the above sense) of the sequence and the alphabet, each letter appears exactly once.

b) For the English alphabet (26 letters), prove that whatever sequence of 26 different letters is added to the alphabet, the result always contains at least two identical letters.

9.2   The sequence of letters of the Russian alphabet

АБВГДЕЁЖЗИЙКЛМНОПРСТУФХЦЧШЩЪЫЬЭЮЯ

is added 1949^{1999} times (in the way described in the previous problem) to the word КРИПТОША. The result is the word АНАЛИТИК. Find this sequence. How many times should the sequence be added to the word АНАЛИТИК (analyst) to get the word КРИПТОША (Ciphy)?

9.3   A message in Russian is converted to a sequence of digits according to the rule

А	Б	В	Г	Д	Е	Ё	Ж	З	И	Й	К	Л	М	Н	О	П
01	02	03	04	05	06	07	08	09	10	11	12	13	14	15	16	17

Р	С	Т	У	Ф	Х	Ц	Ч	Ш	Щ	Ъ	Ы	Ь	Э	Ю	Я
18	19	20	21	22	23	24	25	26	27	28	29	30	31	32	33

The sequence is broken (from right to left) into groups of three digits. Considering such a group as a three-digit number, we multiply each group by 77 and keep only the last three decimal digits of the result. Thus, the following sequence is obtained

$$317564404970017677550547850355$$

Reconstruct the message.

10.1 Ciphy's face is depicted by coloring each cell of a 15×15 array in black or in white. We say that several consecutive cells of the same color of the same row or column form *a strip*. The length of a strip is the number of cells it contains. The lengths of black strips for each row (from top to bottom) are as follows: 9; 11; $1, 1$; $2, 3, 3, 2$; $2, 2$; $2, 1, 1, 1, 2$; $2, 1, 2$; $2, 2$; $1, 5, 1$; $2, 3, 2$; $2, 2$; 7; $1, 1$; $6, 6$; $1, 4, 1, 4, 1$. The lengths of black strips in each column (from left to right) are: 1; $5, 1$; $9, 2$; $2, 2, 2$; $2, 1, 2, 2$; $2, 1, 1, 1, 1, 2$; $2, 1, 2, 3$; $2, 2, 2, 1, 1$; $2, 1, 2, 3$; $2, 1, 1, 1, 1, 2$; $2, 1, 2, 2$; $2, 2, 2$; $9, 2$; $5, 1$; 1. Two black strips of the same row or column are separated by at least one white cell.

Reconstruct the portrait of Ciphy.

10.2 Solve the equation

$$x^2 + y^2 + z^2 + xy - yz - 5 = u^2 + v^2 + w^2 - vw + uw + 2u - 2v + 2w,$$

where the variables are allowed to take only the following values:

x	y	z	u	v	w
0	-1	1	-1	0	0
1	2	2	0	3	1

10.3 The letters of the reduced alphabet (I and J are treated as one letter)

ABCDEFGHIKLMNOPQRSTUVWXYZ

are written into cells of a 5×5 square as follows. First, the letters of *a keyword* are written in along the spaces from left to right, beginning from the upper left corner. The only rule about the keyword is that it is a word of six different letters. After writing the keyword, the remaining letters of the alphabet are written in the succeeding cells in their natural order. To encrypt an English word we replace each letter of the word with an ordered pair of digits: the numbers of the row and column containing this letter. The sequence of digits thus obtained is then written in the reverse order, and each pair of digits (from left to right) is replaced with the corresponding letter of the square. Find the keyword if you know that the word HANDWRITING is encrypted as PVMTMEDWVAH.

10.4 Denote by s_n the last digit in the decimal representation of the number $x_n = 1 + 2 + 3 + \cdots + n$, $n \in \mathbb{N}$. In the sequence $\{s_n\}$ we mark all the numbers equal to 1. All the marked 1's are numbered from left to right as $1, 2, \ldots$. For example, s_1 gets the number 1. With the kth element "1" we associate a permutation p_k of ten digits $0, 1, \ldots, 9$ according to the following rule. We write out the kth element 1 and the succeeding numbers of the sequence $\{s_n\}$ until we meet a digit that we have already written out. In so doing, if not all the digits $0, 1, \ldots, 9$ have been written out, we add the remaining digits written in the natural order.

a) prove that the sequence $\{s_n\}$ is periodic; find its smallest positive period;

b) prove that the sequence of permutations $p_1, p_2, \ldots$ is periodic; find its least positive period.

10.5 To encrypt an English text, we break it into groups of ten letters and rearrange the letters of a kth group by using the permutation p_k described in the previous problem. For example, the permutation 1340596782 encrypts ABCDEFGHIJ to BDEAFJGHIC. Reconstruct the following encrypted passage from L. Carroll:

```
LRHAGLITSA  DAACITHETN  TTDIIHSMEI  VTANISHEDQ
IEOULTSWLY  EGINBGINNW  TEIETHHNDO  TFHITAILAN
EDGDNNIWIT  TWIRHHEGNH  CMIARHEINE  SDOMETIMEA
TREFHETRES  OGAHTFITDO  ERNRCLAOLL
```

11.1 A certain letter composes from 10.5 to 11 percent of a certain text. Find the minimum possible length of such a text.

11.2 A passage from an eminent author was first written out with no punctuation and no breaks between words. Then the resulting string of letters was encrypted with a simple substitution cipher (each letter of the passage was replaced with the corresponding letter of the ciphertext; identical letters were replaced with identical letters; one ciphertext letter did not correspond to different letters of the passage). After that, the original string was encrypted in a different way. Namely, it was broken successively into groups of equal length; then the letters of each group were rearranged according to the same rule. Reconstruct the passage if the two ciphertexts are as follows:

л г н а б е я х ю б к х е б я н д б н б л н м х н м в к ц е е н р х
е о н п г ю м д я н р ч н б х ш я в н м е б х к н н

п х ф у с б л п ш щ ь а ъ б п п ф ь э б щ п б с в л ф э б е ф щ й б
ф ю э а ъ я б у б р п б ь ю б е э ц щ ь б л б п ф щ

We deliberately do not specify from which cipher each ciphertext is obtained. Yet it is known that the ciphertext ШВМВМРЖЭЭСВХ БКЗНДЭЬ is obtained from that simple substitution cipher, and the plaintext is author's name plus the title of the work the passage is from.

11.3 The English letters are represented as five-character sequences of zeros and ones as follows: A = 00000, ..., O = 01110, ..., Z = 11001. The sequences are suitable for transmission by using a five-wire cable: each character is transmitted through its own wire. At the receiving end, Ciphy randomly rearranged the wires; as a result, the following unintelligible word was obtained: MQOCM. Determine the actual word that was transmitted.

11.4 We say that a cell of a 8 × 8 square is "good" if the other cells can be covered by pairwise nonoverlapping 3 × 1 rectangles.

a) Find all "good" cells of the square.

b) A message is encrypted through the use of *a keyword*. Suppose the keyword was ИКСИ. Each letter of the message would be transformed to the corresponding letter of the sequence ИКСИИКСИ...; for example, if the seventh letter of the message was A, then it would be replaced with the seventh letter of the sequence, С. Now, in our case, if the seventh letter is Б, then it is replaced with Т, В is replaced with У, ..., Я with Р. The keyword is written into "good" cells.

Then the encrypted message is written, by rows, into the remaining cells. The result is shown in the figure. Determine the keyword and reconstruct the message.

щ	е	д	е	ю	у	я	б
б	в	ш	а	р	ш	д	н
п	ь	р	щ	е	у	в	ё
ъ	й	л	ё	и	ж	щ	е
д	е	ю	у	в	к	ч	ч
с	б	с	г	е	ь	р	е
ш	в	й	е	с	в	ь	о
з	ю	ь	ь	а	ь	з	ь

11.5 Four equal rectangles of width 100 mm and height 90 mm are put into the four corners of a square with side 269 mm (one rectangle in each corner). Find out if it is possible to interchange the rectangles standing in the opposite corners by moving them within the square. Of course, the rectangles must never overlap.

6. Answers, hints, solutions

1.1   Let the cells of a $2n \times 2n$ table be divided into disjoint, four-cell groups such that a 90° rotation of the table around its center takes a cell of a group to another cell of the same group. The groups for a 6×6 square are shown in Figure 12. Cells of the same group are marked identically. In the general case, we have n^2 groups. Suppose the grille is placed on the table with its marked edge up. It is clear that apertures are to be so chosen that exactly one cell of each group is beneath an aperture.

Thus, we have n^2 groups and four possibilities to select an aperture for each. The answer is 4^{n^2}.

1.2   One can easily note that $f(x) = (x^2 + 3x + 1)(x^4 + x + 1) + 2$. Hence $f(x_1) = f(x_2)$, where x_1, x_2 are the roots of $x^2 + 3x + 1$. We

1	2	3	4	5	1
5	6	7	8	6	2
4	8	9	9	7	3
3	7	9	9	8	4
2	6	8	7	6	5
1	5	4	3	2	1

Figure 12

have

E	C	G	U	C	T	U	J	K	H	V
5	3	7	21	3	20	21	10	11	8	22
3	1	5	19	1	18	19	8	9	6	20
C	A	E	S	A	R	S	H	I	F	T

The answer is CAESARSHIFT.

1.3 *Answer.* Starting with $n = 54$.

1.4 Factoring m and d into primes gives $d = 6 = 2 \cdot 3$; $m = 6930 = 2 \cdot 3 \cdot 3 \cdot 5 \cdot 7 \cdot 11$. Let $t = m/d = 3 \cdot 5 \cdot 7 \cdot 11$. Let us find all the divisors q of t such that $q = 3^x 5^y 7^z 11^u$ and each of the numbers x, y, z, u is either 0 or 1. Then q and t/q are coprime numbers. By putting $a = dq$ and $b = dt/q$, we obtain all the desired ordered pairs (a, b). It is clear that $\gcd(a, b) = d$ and $\operatorname{lcm}(a, b) = dqt/q = dt = dm/d = m$. We see that the number of ordered pairs equals the number of divisors q of the form $3^x 5^y 7^z 11^u$. Obviously there is a one-to-one correspondence between such divisors and strings of 1s and 0s of length 4. The number of such strings is $2^4 = 16$ (each position of the strings can be filled with either 1 or 0). In the general case, we have $m/d = p^i r^j \ldots s^h$, where $p, r, \ldots, s$ are pairwise distinct primes and $i, j, \ldots, h$ are positive integers. If q is a divisor of t, then $q = p^x r^y \ldots, s^z$; if we want q and t/q to be coprime, then x equals either 0 or i, y is either 0 or j, etc. Hence, q can take 2^k different values, where k is the number of prime divisors of t.

Answer. 16 ordered pairs (a, b). For arbitrary m and d, there are exactly 2^k ordered pairs, where k is the number of prime divisors of m/d.

1.5   Upon inspection of the third row, one can note that $\mathtt{D} = 0$ because $\mathtt{D} + \mathtt{T} = \mathtt{T}$. Considering the first column, we get $\mathtt{E} = 1$. The last column gives $\mathtt{C} = 2$. We have

$$
\begin{array}{ccccc}
\mathtt{20} & \times & \mathtt{N} & = & \mathtt{2P2} \\
+ & & \times & & - \\
\mathtt{II} & + & \mathtt{I} & = & \mathtt{OY} \\
= & & = & & = \\
\mathtt{10P} & + & \mathtt{TR} & = & \mathtt{1T0}
\end{array}
$$

Looking at the second row, we see that $\mathtt{O} > \mathtt{I}$. From the first column, we find $\mathtt{I} = 7$. Then, using the second row, we get $\mathtt{O} = 8$ and $\mathtt{Y} = 4$. Replacing the letters with the digits we already know gives

$$
\begin{array}{ccccc}
\mathtt{28} & \times & \mathtt{N} & = & \mathtt{2P2} \\
+ & & \times & & - \\
\mathtt{77} & + & \mathtt{7} & = & \mathtt{84} \\
= & & = & & = \\
\mathtt{10P} & + & \mathtt{TR} & = & \mathtt{1T8}
\end{array}
$$

Now we can find successively $\mathtt{P} = 5$, $\mathtt{N} = 9$, $\mathtt{T} = 6$, $\mathtt{R} = 3$. Arranging the letters in the order of increasing magnitudes of the corresponding digits, we obtain the word "decryption".

1.6   *Answer.* For example, *cbcacbc*. Denote by $\overline{\varphi(P)}$ the sequence $\varphi(P)$ written in the reverse order. Then

$$
\varphi(cbcacbc) = \overline{\varphi(bcacbc)} = \overline{\varphi(cacbc)a\varphi(cacbc)}
$$
$$
= \overline{\overline{\varphi(acbc)}a\overline{\varphi(acbc)}} = \overline{\overline{cbcacbc}} = \overline{cbcacbc} = cbcacbc.
$$

It can be shown that any valid password is of the form

$$
P = \begin{cases}
cb\underbrace{c\ldots\ldots c}_{k \text{ times}}acb\underbrace{c\ldots\ldots c}_{k \text{ times}}, & k \text{ is odd;} \\[2ex]
b\underbrace{c\ldots\ldots c}_{k \text{ times}}ab\underbrace{c\ldots\ldots c}_{k \text{ times}}, & k \text{ is even.}
\end{cases}
$$

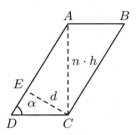

Figure 13

2.1   Consider one turn of the strip; in the unrolled configuration this turn is shown in Figure 13. From C drop a perpendicular, CE, to AD. We are given that $CE = d$. The angle DAC is $90° - \alpha$. Hence $AC = d/\cos\alpha$. Since the height of each row is h, we see that one turn contains $n = d/(h \cdot \cos\alpha)$ letters.

Answer. To read the text, one should cut the strip into parts such that each part contains $n = d/(h \cdot \cos\alpha)$ letters. Then the parts are to be put together to form a parallelogram with the height AC.

2.2   It follows from the conditions that the plaintext consists of two five-digit groups, $A_1A_2A_3A_4A_5$ and $B_1B_2B_3B_4B_5$. Let C_1C_2 be the last two digits of the sum of the corresponding five-digit integers. Denote by $a \oplus b$ the last digit of the sum $a + b$. Let D be the second digit from the left (the number of tens) of the sum $A_5 + B_5$. We have $A_5 \oplus B_5 = C_2$ and $(A_4 \oplus B_4) \oplus D = C_1$.

Denote the first term of the arithmetic progression by Γ_1 and the increment by X. Then

(1) $A_1 \oplus \Gamma_1 = 4,$

(2) $A_2 \oplus (\Gamma_1 + X) = 2,$

(3) $A_3 \oplus (\Gamma_1 + 2X) = 3,$

(4) $A_4 \oplus (\Gamma_1 + 3X) = 4,$

(5) $A_5 \oplus (\Gamma_1 + 4X) = 6,$

(6) $B_1 \oplus (\Gamma_1 + 5X) = 1,$

(7) $B_2 \oplus (\Gamma_1 + 6X) = 4,$

(8) $$B_3 \oplus (\Gamma_1 + 7X) = 0,$$

(9) $$B_4 \oplus (\Gamma_1 + 8X) = 5,$$

(10) $$B_5 \oplus (\Gamma_1 + 9X) = 3,$$

(11) $$((A_4 \oplus B_4) \oplus D) \oplus (\Gamma_1 + 10X) = 1,$$

(12) $$(A_5 \oplus B_5) \oplus (\Gamma_1 + 11X) = 3.$$

We write $A \equiv B$ if A and B yield the same remainder when divided by 10. Then the relation $A \oplus B = C$ is the same as $(A + B) \equiv C$. If $A \equiv B$ and $C \equiv D$, then $A + B \equiv C + D$ and $A - B \equiv C - D$. Obviously, $A \equiv A$ because the remainder is unique.

It follows from (4), (5), (9), and (10) that

(13) $$A_4 \equiv 4 - (\Gamma_1 + 3X),$$

(14) $$A_5 \equiv 6 - (\Gamma_1 + 4X),$$

(15) $$B_4 \equiv 5 - (\Gamma_1 + 8X),$$

(16) $$B_5 \equiv 3 - (\Gamma_1 + 9X).$$

Substituting these into (11) and (12), we get $9 + D - \Gamma_1 - X \equiv 1$ and $9 - \Gamma_1 - 2X \equiv 3$. This gives

(17) $$X \equiv (-2 - D),$$

(18) $$\Gamma_1 \equiv 2D.$$

Using these expressions in (1), (2), (3), (13), (14), (6), (7), (8), (15), (16), we find the digits of the plaintext to be

$$A_1 \equiv 4 - 2D, \quad A_2 \equiv 4 - D, \quad A_3 \equiv 7,$$
$$A_4 \equiv D, \quad A_5 \equiv 4 + 2D,$$
$$B_1 \equiv 1 + 3D, \quad B_2 \equiv 6 + 4D, \quad B_3 \equiv 4 + 5D,$$
$$B_4 \equiv 1 + 6D, \quad B_5 \equiv 1 + 7D.$$

Thus, the plaintext is one of the following

$$4470416411 \ (D = 0)$$
$$2371640978 \ (D = 1)$$

2.3 *Answer.* a is any positive integer; b is any positive integer that is not divisible by either 2 or 5.

Hint. Denote by $f(x)$ the residue of $F(x)$ modulo 10. For the plaintext to be determined uniquely it is necessary and sufficient that different values of x yield different residues $f(x)$. Therefore the sequence $f(0), f(1), \ldots, f(9)$ is a permutation of the digits $0, 1, \ldots, 9$. We have

$$f(0) = r_{10}(b(a + 0)), \qquad f(1) = r_{10}(b(a + 1)),$$
$$f(2) = r_{10}(b(a + 2)), \qquad f(3) = r_{10}(b(a + 9)),$$
$$f(4) = r_{10}(b(a + 8)), \qquad f(5) = r_{10}(b(a + 5)),$$
$$f(6) = r_{10}(b(a + 6)), \qquad f(7) = r_{10}(b(a + 7)),$$
$$f(8) = r_{10}(b(a + 4)), \qquad f(9) = r_{10}(b(a + 3)).$$

Here $r_{10}(y)$ is the remainder when y is divided by 10.

For even b, $f(x)$ is even. For b divisible by 5, $f(x)$ is either 0 or 5. Now it can be easily shown that for any a and b (b is not divisible by either 2 or 5) the transformation $F(x)$ has a unique inverse.

2.4 Denote by $S(n)$ the residue of the sum of the numbers corresponding to the first n letters of the alphabet modulo 26. Thus $n = 1, \ldots, 26$ and $0 \leq S(n) \leq 25$.

If one of the numbers $S(1), S(2), \ldots, S(26)$ is zero, say $S(t)$, then the lock opens when the corresponding t keys are pressed.

Suppose now that all the numbers $S(1), S(2), \ldots, S(26)$ are different from zero; then at least two of them, $S(k)$ and $S(m)$, are equal (let $k < m$). In this case, to open the lock, it is sufficient to strike all those letters whose position in the alphabet is from $k + 1$ to m inclusive.

2.5 First we convert the cryptograms to sequences of integers using the correspondence between the alphabet characters and residues modulo 26: A $\leftrightarrow$ 1, B $\leftrightarrow$ 2, ..., Y $\leftrightarrow$ 25, Z $\leftrightarrow$ 0. We have

W	Q	U	Z	J	S	U	N	J	E	T	I	X	N	I	B
23	17	21	0	10	19	21	14	10	5	20	9	24	14	9	2

N	G	Q	B
14	7	17	2

I	X	K	Z	V	M	H	B	J	Q	T	F	V	J	H	M
9	24	11	0	22	13	8	2	10	17	20	6	22	10	8	13

Q	W	I	C
17	23	9	3

In what follows, all arithmetical operations are assumed to be modulo 26. Subtracting the first cryptogram character by character from the second, we get

(1)

12	7	16	0	12	20	13	14	0	12	0	23	24	22	25

11	3	16	18	1

It is remarkable that the result bears no information on the enciphering string and obviously coincides with the difference of the plaintexts. All we have to do is to add the combination QUESTIONS to each nine-character segment of the string (1) and see which segment yields an intelligible text. The results of the 12 additions are

(2)

1	2	3	4	5	6	7	8	9	10	11	17
3	24	7	17	3	11	4	5	17	3	17	14
2	11	21	7	15	8	9	21	7	21	18	19
21	5	17	25	18	19	5	17	5	2	3	1
19	5	13	6	7	19	5	19	16	17	15	18
6	14	7	8	20	6	20	17	18	16	19	5
3	22	23	9	21	9	6	7	3	8	20	12
2	3	15	1	15	12	13	11	14	0	18	5
2	14	0	14	11	12	10	13	25	17	4	6
19	5	19	16	17	15	18	4	22	9	11	20

Upon subtraction of the first cryptogram from the second, we get

(3)

14	19	10	0	14	6	13	12	0	14	0	3	2	4	1

15	23	10	8	25

As before, adding QUESTIONS to all nine-character segments of (3), we get

(4)

1	2	3	4	5	6	7	8	9	10	11	12
5	10	1	17	5	23	4	3	17	5	17	20
14	5	21	9	1	8	7	21	9	21	24	23
15	5	19	11	18	17	5	19	5	8	7	9
19	7	25	6	5	19	7	19	22	21	23	20
8	0	7	6	20	8	20	23	22	24	21	9
15	22	21	9	23	9	12	11	13	10	24	6
2	1	15	3	15	18	17	19	16	4	12	25
0	14	2	14	17	16	18	15	3	11	24	22
19	7	19	22	21	23	20	8	16	3	1	18

Converting the numbers in (2) and (4) to alphabetical characters, we obtain

1	2	3	4	5	6	7	8	9	10	11	12
C	X	G	Q	C	K	D	E	Q	C	Q	N
B	K	U	G	O	H	I	U	G	U	R	S
U	E	Q	Y	R	S	E	Q	E	B	C	A
S	E	M	F	G	S	E	S	P	Q	O	R
F	N	G	H	T	F	T	Q	R	P	S	E
C	V	W	I	U	I	F	G	C	H	T	L
B	C	O	A	O	L	M	K	N	Z	R	E
B	N	Z	N	K	L	J	M	Y	Q	D	F
S	E	S	P	Q	O	R	D	V	I	K	T

1	2	3	4	5	6	7	8	9	10	11	12
E	J	A	Q	E	W	D	C	Q	E	Q	T
N	E	U	I	A	H	G	U	I	U	X	W
O	E	S	K	R	Q	E	S	E	H	G	I
S	G	Y	F	E	S	G	S	V	U	W	T
H	Z	G	F	T	H	T	W	V	X	U	I
O	V	U	I	W	I	L	K	M	J	X	F
B	A	O	C	O	R	Q	S	P	D	L	Y
Z	N	B	N	Q	P	R	O	C	K	X	V
S	G	S	V	U	W	T	H	P	C	A	R

The columns with intelligible text are seen at once. Denoting by dots yet unknown letters of the plaintexts, we get

plaintext 1: ... EARETWOQUESTIONS

plaintext 2: ... QUESTIONSARELEFT

Obviously, in plaintext 1 nothing else fit but THERE, or maybe WHERE. Assuming it to be THERE, we determine the first four characters of the enciphering string and thus find the beginning of plaintext 2 to be FOUR. If plaintext 1 starts with WHERE, then the first four letters of plaintext 2 are ZOUR that makes no sense.

Answer. THEREARETWOQUESTIONS and FOURQUESTIONSARELEFT.

2.6   For each letter of the ciphertext we try successively K, E, and Y as the corresponding letter of the key sequence. We have

	S	F	U	J	L	Y	N	N	P	S	T	K	T	C	F	X
K	H	U	J	Y	A	N	C	C	E	H	I	Z	I	R	U	M
E	N	A	P	E	G	T	I	I	K	N	O	F	O	X	A	S
Y	T	G	V	K	M	Z	O	O	Q	T	U	L	U	D	G	Y

From each columns we choose a letter for a meaningful text to appear. The plaintext is HAVEANICEHOLIDAY.

3.1   In this cipher, different plaintext letters are replaced with different ciphertext letters while identical plaintext letters are replaced with identical ones. Therefore two different plaintexts cannot yield the same ciphertext, and identical plaintexts produce the same ciphertext. Thus, we are to find the number of iterations to make for the word **SECRET** to appear again. This number is exactly the desired number of different words.

The first letter of the word becomes **S** again after every other iteration, i.e., we can say that the period of **S** is 2. The periods of **E**, **C**, **R**, and **T** are 9, 5, 3, and 7, respectively. The least common multiple of $2, 3, 5, 7, 9$ is 630.

Answer. 630.

3.2 Let the letters in a group be numbered as $1, 2, \ldots, 12$. Bob receives them in the order 2, 4, 6, 8, 10, 12, 1, 3, 5, 7, 9, 11. When Oscar receives them, they are rearranged as 4, 8, 12, 3, 7, 11, 2, 6, 10, 1, 5, 9. After Alice has encrypted the message with her simple substitution, she gets the following

```
f z b a w d c z x e x y
f x y c a z v x e c g y
s e a g w e x a z q g s
j s i v d w i i e v w i
```

Each transformation mentioned in the statement of the problem, is one-to-one, i.e., different letters are represented by different letters and identical letters are represented by identical letters. Therefore, in the ciphertext that Alice is about to send to Bob, we should find the group that contains as many pairs of identical letters as the word **CRYPTOGRAPHY** does. Obviously, this is the second group. The rest of the cryptogram can be then easily solved using frequency analysis.

Answer.

```
C O N T E M P O R A R Y
C R Y P T O G R A P H Y
I S T H E A R T O F H I
D I N G M E S S A G E S
```

3.3 Let us show that 20 is indeed a period. The last digits of two positive integers, a and b, coincide whenever $a - b$ is exactly divisible by 10. Thus all we have to do is to prove that 10 divides $(n + 20)^{n+20} - n^n$ for any positive integer n. Since $(p - q)$ divides $p^k - q^k$, we see that $((n+20) - 20) = 20$ divides $(n+20)^{n+20} - n^{n+20}$.

Moreover, $n^{n+20} - n^n = n^n(n^{20} - 1) = n^n((n^4)^5 - 1)$ is divisible by $n(n^4 - 1)$ for any $n > 1$. We have

$$n(n^4 - 1) = n(n-1)(n+1)(n^2 + 1)$$
$$= n(n-1)(n+2)((n+2)(n-2) + 5)$$
$$= (n-2)(n-1)n(n+1)(n+2) + 5(n-1)n(n+1).$$

Here each summand is even because it contains $n(n+1)$. In addition, the first summand is a product of five consecutive integers and thus is divisible by 5; the second is also divisible by 5 because it contains the factor 5. Consequently, 10 divides $n^{n+20} - n^n$. Therefore, the number

$$(n+20)^{n+20} - n^n = ((n+20)^{n+20} - n^{n+20}) + (n^{n+20} - n^n)$$

is divisible by 10 because each summand is.

The proof that 20 is the least period is straightforward, i.e., we simply write out the first 20 numbers of our sequence:

$$1\ 4\ 7\ 6\ 5\ 3\ 6\ 9\ 0\ 1\ 6\ 3\ 6\ 5\ 6\ 7\ 4\ 9\ 0$$

3.4   To begin with let us recover the sequence of digits to which our message was first converted. In this sequence a digit with odd position number is one of the following: 0, 1, 2, and 3. From each digit at odd position in the cryptogram we subtract 0, 1, 2, 3 reducing the result modulo 10. This gives us variant values of the numbers $C_k, C_{k+3}, C_{k+5}, \ldots$ used for encryption. We have

position k	1	3	5	7	9	11	13	15	17	19	21	23	25	27
cryptogram	2	3	8	7	1	4	8	6	6	0	1	3	5	8
0	2	3	8	7	1	4	8	6	6	0	1	3	5	8
1	1	2	7	6	0	3	7	5	5	9	0	2	4	7
2	0	1	6	5	9	2	6	4	4	8	9	1	3	6
3	9	0	5	4	8	1	5	3	3	7	8	0	2	5

As shown in the solution of Problem 3.3, the smallest period of the sequence $\{C_n\}$ is 20. According to the table, the digit added to the fifth digit of our message can be 5, 6, 7, or 8. The digit added to the 25th digit of the message can be 2, 3, 4, or 5. Hence $\Gamma_5 = \Gamma_{25} = 5$.

The digit 5 occurs twice within a period of the sequence, that is, $C_5 = C_{15} = 5$. Thus we have to decide between these cases. If $\Gamma_5 = C_5$, then $\Gamma_7 = C_7 = 3$ but this contradicts the variant values of Γ_7 calculated above. Suppose $\Gamma_5 = C_{15}$; then the encrypting sequence is 16365674901476563690016365674, which correlates well with the calculated variant values. Subtracting the encrypting sequence from the cryptogram and reducing modulo 10, we get

cryptogram	23	39	86	72	16	45	81	60	67	06	17	31	55	88
enciphering sequence	16	36	56	74	90	14	76	56	36	90	16	36	56	74
numeric message	17	03	30	08	26	31	15	14	31	16	01	05	09	14
message	С	В	Я	З	Ь	-	П	О	-	Р	А	Д	И	О

4.1 The ciphertext consists of 48 letters. Hence the fourth time the grille was placed upon the paper not all the apertures were filled. Thus the blank cells of the cryptogram clearly show where these "extra" apertures were. We do not know the location of the other three apertures. In the figure, the known apertures are marked with an asterisk. Since the letters were written in from left to right and from top to bottom, we conclude that these three apertures must appear in the first row or in the first five cells of the second row. Since each cell on the paper becomes visible for exactly one aperture, it is clear that the possible locations of the three apertures are among those indicated by a question mark in the figure.

	?				?	
		?	?	*		*
*			*		*	
		*		*		
					*	
*		*	*		*	

A 90° rotation takes one marked cell in the first row into the other, hence exactly one of them corresponds to an aperture. Thus we have two cases to consider. A meaningful text appears when the second question mark in the first row is taken to represent an aperture. The plaintext is

johndevotedalotoftimetomathematicsandbookkeeping

4.2   In the English language, there are only two one-letter words, I and A. Thus 15 stands for one of them and 7 for the other. The third line of the cryptogram ends with 23 2 7. Therefore, 7 is A because there are only few three-letter words ending with I. The combination 3 18 2 appears four times. It is improbable it represents an exotic word, say ELF. Since it appears so many times within a short passage, it is reasonable to assume it to be one of the following: THE, AND, HAS, SAY, ALL. But A is 7, hence, most probably, 3 18 2 represents THE. To support this idea note that 2 is the prevailing character in the passage while the letter E predominates all other letters in ordinary English texts. The word 3 11 shows that the value of 11 is O. With the knowledge of so many letters, the rest is easy. The passage reads

I SENT A MESSAGE TO THE FISH

I TOLD THEM ''THIS IS WHAT I WISH.''

THE LITTLE FISHES OF THE SEA

THEY SENT AN ANSWER BACK TO ME.

THE LITTLE FISHES ANSWER WAS

''WE CANNOT DO IT, SIR, BECAUSE.''

4.3   *Answer.* $\cos 36° = (1 + \sqrt{5})/4 = 0.8$.

4.4   Let the letters of the Latin alphabet be numbered as follows: A is 1, ..., Z is 24. Let x be an integer from 1 to 24. Denote by $f(x)$ the number to which x is mapped in the second step. The interchangeability of the two steps can be expressed as

$$f(x + 1) = f(x) + 1, \quad f(x + 1) - f(x) = 1.$$

This shows that any neighboring numbers (x and $x+1$) remain neighboring under the transformation f. Thus f is also a shift. There are 24 shifts to try. Only one of them yields an intelligible text.

Answer. INTER ARMA SILENT MUSAE.

4.6 Note that $A_{k+1} - A_k = (k+1)^3 - k^3 + 2$ for any positive integer k. Adding up these equalities for $k = 1, 2, \ldots, (n-1)$, we get $A_n - A_1 = n^3 - 3 + 2n$. Since $A_1 = 3$, we have $A_n = n^3 + 2n$.

Obviously, both for decryption and encryption, we can use the remainders of the numbers A_{101}, A_{102}, A_{103}, A_{104}, A_{105}, A_{106} when divided by 30, and not the numbers themselves. For any integer i, we can write

$$(100 + i)^3 + 2(100 + i) = i^3 + 2i + 30z.$$

Therefore the remainders are

A_{100}	A_{101}	A_{102}	A_{103}	A_{104}	A_{105}	A_{106}
0	3	12	3	12	15	18

The rest is as follows:

cryptogram	К	Е	Н	З	Э	Р	Е
	9	5	12	7	27	15	5
enciphering string	0	3	12	3	12	15	18
plaintext	9	2	0	4	15	0	17
	К	В	А	Д	Р	А	Т

Answer. КВАДРАТ (SQUARE).

5.1 When divided by 7, y^2 yields the remainders 0, 1, 2, 4; therefore, the remainders of $3x^2$ can be 0, 3, 6, 5. Evidently, the residue of $3x^2 - y^2$ modulo 7 must be 1. This entails that either $x^2 \equiv 1$ and $y^2 \equiv 2 \mod 7$ or $x^2 \equiv 4 \mod 7$ and $y^2 \equiv 4 \mod 7$. Thus, we have the following series of pairs (x, y) to try: 1) $x \in \{13, 15, 20\}$, $y \in \{10, 11, 17, 18\}$; 2) $x \in \{12, 16, 19\}$, $y \in \{12, 16, 19\}$. For each pair we check if z is in the range $[10, 20]$.

Answer. $(12, 16, 11)$, $(13, 17, 17)$, $(13, 18, 12)$.

5.4 In the second case, the cryptanalyst knows the ciphertext equivalents for the letters i, n, s, t, a, c, e; in the first case he knows the same letters except c. Thus the cryptanalyst is more likely to succeed in the second case.

5.6   The letters M, O, S, C, O, W stand right in this order in each cryptogram, that is,

$$JP^MI^OUQ^SVZ^CA^OBX^WE$$
$$R^MFH^OBD^SKO^CG^OLM^WNO$$
$$FF^MUV^OYC^SOP^CV^OA^WKQ$$

It is reasonable to assume that the encryption algorithm consists in putting each letter of a plaintext between one- or two-letter combinations. Combinations are selected according to a rule known to the correspondents.

In this cipher, the first letter of a plaintext always coincides with the second or the third letter of the cryptogram. Inspecting the beginnings of the cryptograms, we see that the first and the third cryptograms represent the same plaintext, whose first letter is B. The next common letter one or two spaces after B is E. Proceeding in this manner, we get

BETTER LATE THAN NEVER

Answer. Better late than never. First think, then speak.

6.1   Since each of the 1997 users is connected with exactly N other users, $1997 \cdot N/2$ links between them are required. For this number to be an integer, N must be even.

Now we will prove that for any even N a network with specified properties exists. Let $N = 2T$. Suppose the users are arranged along a circle. Let each of them be connected with the next T users proceeding clockwise and with the next T users proceeding counterclockwise. This is a network we need.

6.2   Let us prove the following statement. Each integer from 1 to 1997 appears on the main diagonal exactly once. Assume the opposite, that is, let there exist $a \in \{1, \ldots, 1997\}$ such that all the numbers on the diagonal are different from a. By symmetry, a appears in the table an even number of times. On the other hand, each row contains exactly one a. The number of rows is odd, hence the number of occurrences of a is also odd. This contradiction shows that all the integers from 1 to 1997 are present on the diagonal. To complete the proof, note that the main diagonal consists of 1997 cells.

The answer is $1 + 2 + 3 + \cdots + 1997 = 1995003$.

6.3 *Answer.* CONTENTS LIST AND DETAILED INDEX ENSURE THAT USERS CAN EASILY FIND THE UNIT THEY NEED.

Hint. Suppose that the substitution cipher replaces a plaintext letter α with a ciphertext letter β. The number of occurrences of β in the first ciphertext equals the number of occurrences of α in the second ciphertext.

6.4 a) Associate numbers with the Russian alphabetical characters as follows: А is 0, Б is 1, etc. The word ОЛИМПИАДА now becomes 15 12 9 13 16 9 0 4 0. Originally the arm is set at А; for the arm to be set at 0, gear 1 must be rotated 15 positions counterclockwise. After that, to point the arm at Л we must rotate the gear 45 positions, etc. The whole encryption looks as follows:

	1	2	3	4	5	6	7	8	9
letter on gear 1	О	Л	И	М	П	И	А	Д	А
number of positions to rotate (counted from the original configuration)	15	45	75	79	82	108	132	136	165
digit on gear 2	5	5	5	1	8	2	8	4	5
digit on gear 3	1	2	5	2	5	3	6	3	4

Thus, the word ОЛИМПИАДА is encrypted as

515355128523864354.

b) Suppose that now the arm is pointing at А; let t_k be the number of positions gear 1 must be rotated to set the arm at the letter with number k, $k = 1, 2, \ldots$.

Suppose the arm points at a letter with number k on gear 1; denote by a_k and b_k the corresponding digits on gears 2, 3, respectively.

Then, taking into account the initial positions of the gears, we can write

$$(1) \qquad t_k = 10m_k - a_k, \quad k = 1, 2, \ldots,$$

$$(2) \qquad t_k = 7m_k + b_k, \quad k = 1, 2, \ldots .$$

Here m_k and n_k are nonnegative integers.

Note that $1 = 7 \cdot 3 - 10 \cdot 2$. We have

$$a_k = 7 \cdot (3a_k) - 10 \cdot (2a_k), \quad k = 1, 2, \ldots,$$

$$b_k = 7 \cdot (3b_k) - 10 \cdot (2b_k), \quad k = 1, 2, \ldots .$$

Substituting these into (1) and (2), we get

$$t_k = 10(m_k + 2a_k) - 7 \cdot (3a_k), \quad k = 1, 2, \ldots,$$

$$t_k = 7 \cdot (n_k + 3b_k) - 10 \cdot (2b_k), \quad k = 1, 2, \ldots .$$

Therefore

$$10(m_k + 2a_k) - 7 \cdot (3a_k) = 7 \cdot (n_k + 3b_k) - 10 \cdot (2b_k).$$

Both sides of this equation are divisible by 70. Therefore we can represent them as $70s_k$, where s_k is a nonnegative integer. We have

$$m_k = 7s_k - 2(a_k + b_k), \quad k = 1, 2, \ldots,$$

$$n_k = 10s_k - 3(a_k + b_k), \quad k = 1, 2, \ldots .$$

Upon substitution of the expression for m_k into (1), we arrive at

$$t_k = 70s_k - 21a_k - 20b_k, \quad k = 1, 2, \ldots .$$

Since $0 < t_1 < t_2 < \cdots < t_7$, we finally get

k	1	2	3	4	5	6	7
a_k	2	8	9	8	9	1	1
b_k	4	0	2	3	1	2	1
$-(21a_k + 20b_k)$	-122	-168	-229	-228	-209	-61	-41
t_k	18	42	51	52	71	79	99
letters	C	И	C	T	E	M	A

6.5   *Hint.* Let $1, a_1, \ldots, a_8$ be the nonzero digits arranged along a circle. The digits are numbered clockwise. This arrangement of digits can be uniquely reconstructed given the sequence of pairs $(1, a_1)$,

$(a_1, a_2), \ldots, (a_7, a_8), (a_8, 1)$. This sequence is uniquely determined by the chain

$$(*) \quad \begin{aligned} &(1, a_2), (a_2, a_4), (a_4, a_6), (a_6, a_8), (a_8, a_1), (a_1, a_3), \\ &(a_3, a_5), (a_5, a_7), (a_7, a_1). \end{aligned}$$

Here $a_2, a_3, \ldots, a_8 \in \{2, \ldots, 9\}$ and $a_i \neq a_j$ for $i \neq j$.

Suppose one pair or any two consecutive pairs in $(*)$ are missed; then they can be reconstructed from the remaining pairs.

The chain $(*)$ cannot be determined uniquely if any three pairs are missed. To illustrate this, consider the following segments of a chain of the form $(*)$:

$(a, b)(b, c)(c, d)$ and $(a, c)(c, b)(b, d)$ $(a, b, c, d$ are different digits),

$(a, b)\_(c, d)(d, e)$ and $(a, d)(d, b)\_(c, e)$ $(a, b, c, d, e$ are different digits),

$(a, b)\_(c, d)\_(e, f)$ and $(a, d)(e, b)\_(c, f)$ $(a, b, c, d, e, f$ are different digits).

Given a plaintext and the ciphertext, we have the same pairs (a, b) as those in $(*)$. Here a is a plaintext digit, and b is a digit of the ciphertext.

Answer. To reconstruct uniquely the arrangement of digits along the circle, it is necessary and sufficient that either the plaintext or the ciphertext contains at least seven distinct nonzero digits. (In some sense, this corresponds to $(*)$ with two neighboring pairs missing.)

6.6   For any positive integer n, we have

$$a_{n+2} - a_n = p^{n+4} - p^{n+2} = \begin{cases} 24 \cdot 2^{n-1} & \text{for } p = 2, \\ p^{n+1}(p^3 - p) & \text{for } p \geq 3. \end{cases}$$

The difference $a_{n+2} - a_n$ is divisible by 24 because so is $p^3 - p = (p-1)p(p+1)$.

7.1   It is clear that each node must be connected with at least three other nodes: a configuration where a node A is connected with only two other nodes, B and C, is not permissible because with failure of B and C the node A becomes inaccessible. Thus, the number of lines required is at least $\frac{10\times3}{2} = 15$. The following graph shows that this number is sufficient as well:

With a loss of any two nodes of, say, the inner pentagon, any other two nodes are still connected via the outer pentagon. When one node of each pentagon is disabled, the network is not down because the pentagons are connected by more than two links.

Answer. 15.

7.2   The encryption can be described as follows. Consider a square table of size 10×10. In column j of row i we write the digit to which j is transformed if preceded by i in the password. Since an encrypted password must determine the plain password uniquely, we conclude that each digit $0, \ldots, 9$ occurs in each row exactly once.

Denote by $c_1, \ldots, c_7$ the given encrypted passwords; let p_1, p_2 be the known passwords. An encrypted password has the same length as the password itself, hence neither c_3 nor c_4 could be obtained by encryption of either p_1 or p_2. Assuming that c_1 corresponds to p_1, we get two identical digits in the same row. Therefore the assumption is incorrect. Similarly, it can be shown that none of c_6, c_7 and c_5 could be obtained from p_1. Thus the only possibility left is $p_1 \rightarrow c_2$ and $p_2 \rightarrow c_5$. In this case, we have

	0	1	2	3	4	5	6	7	8	9
0										5
1			3							
2	4	3	7					8		
3		7								
4			2							
5										3
6										
7						4				
8			1	9						
9										

	0	1	2	3	4	5	6	7	8	9
0			6							5
1			3							
2	4	3	7	0	6	2	5	8	9	
3	3	7								
4			2							
5									3	7
6										
7						4				
8			1	9						
9			1							

It is clear that the digit in column nine of row two must be 1. Using the table, we can decrypt c_3 uniquely, and the result is 5830829. The passwords corresponding to c_1, c_4, c_6, c_7 can be disclosed just partially.

Answer. 5393511 decrypts to 5830829. No other encrypted password can be decrypted uniquely.

7.3 *Hint.* The cryptogram consists of $3 \times 17 = 51$ letters. Hence $r = 17$ (for $r = 1$ and $r = 3$ unintelligible texts occur). The constant b just shifts the text cyclically and thus can be dropped. The constant a can take 16 different values; for $a = 10$ we get

1	2	3	4	5	6	7	8	9	10	11	12	13	14	15	16	17
p	r	r	o	c	q	o	y	i	y	t	e	e	l	r	u	g
y	r	e	q	u	i	r	e	c	r	y	p	t	o	l	o	g

1	2	3	4	5	6	7	8	9	10	11	12	13	14	15	16	17
o	y	o	l	s	m	d	n	n	e	w	a	f	e	k	a	g
e	o	f	m	a	n	y	a	s	k	n	o	w	l	e	d	g

1	2	3	4	5	6	7	8	9	10	11	12	13	14	15	16	17
s	c	e	f	r	a	a	a	i	h	o	s	m	m	e	t	t
h	e	m	a	t	i	c	s	r	e	a	s	o	f	m	a	t

The other values of a produce unintelligible combinations.

Answer. Cryptology requires knowledge of many areas of mathematics.

7.4 The succession of knight's moves is specified by numbers

Answer. IN A LAND NOT VERY FAR FROM HERE THERE LIVED A GIRL NAMED LITTLE RED RIDING HOOD.

7.6   Suppose we draw a line (dashed line in Figure 14(a)) keeping the chalk cross-section's sides parallel to the borders of the blackboard. The area of the chalk line is equal to the area of the associated step-line (solid line in Figure 14(a)).

A convex polygon drawn with that piece of chalk is shown in dashed lines in Figure 14(b). The positions of the chalk closest to the edges of the blackboard are marked as U, R, B, and L (Figure 14(b)). The rectangle containing these marked positions is shown as a solid line. It is clear that the area of the rectangle's border is equal to the area of the polygon's border. Moreover, the area of the rectangle is

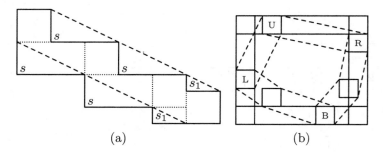

(a)   (b)

Figure 14

larger than the area of the polygon. Thus we have proved that the desired polygon is a rectangle.

Consider a rectangle with sides a and b. Suppose that the area of the rectangle is $10\,000$ cm^2. The area of its border is

$$2a + 2b + 4 = 2a + \frac{20\,000}{a} + 4 = 2\left(\sqrt{a} - \frac{100}{\sqrt{a}}\right)^2 + 404.$$

For this expression to attain minimum, the difference in parentheses must vanish. Thus $a = 100$ and $b = 100$.

Answer. A square of side 1 m; the area of its border is 404 cm^2.

7.7   Denote by G_k a group of k digits; for such a group there exist $k!$ numbers composed of the digits of the group.

The cryptogram does not contain 2 and 9. Hence either these digits form their own group G_2 or they form two groups of one digit each. In both cases, there are exactly two letters represented by these digits.

Since $31 = 1! + 3! + 4!$, we have $\{1, 3, 4, 5, 6, 7, 8, 0\} = G_1 \cup G_3 \cup G_4$. Suppose $G_1 \neq \{1\}$; then we have two cases to consider:

a) $G_4 = \{1, 3, 7, 8\}$, $G_3 = \{0, 5, 6\}$, $G_1 = \{4\}$;

b) $G_4 = \{1, 3, 7, 8\}$, $G_3 = \{4, 5, 6\}$, $G_1 = \{0\}$.

	Case a	Case b		Case a	Case b		Case a	Case b
А	2 (4)	0	К	1738	1738	Х	7183	7183
Б	4 (29)	2 (29)	Л	1783	1783	Ц	7318	7318
В	9 (56)	9 (92)	М	1837	1837	Ч	7381	7381
Г	56 (65)	456	Н	1873	1873	Ш	7813	7813
Д	65 (92)	465	О	3178	3178	Щ	7831	7831
Е	506	546	П	3187	3187	Ъ	8137	8137
Ё	605	564	Р	3718	3718	Ы	8173	8173
Ж	650	645	С	3781	3781	Ь	8317	8317
З	650	654	Т	3817	3817	Э	8371	8371
И	1378	1378	У	3871	3871	Ю	8713	8713
Й	1387	1387	Ф	7138	7138	Я	8731	8731

In case a the plaintext is ЯАЗЧ; in case b we get ЯДАЧ. Looking up these words in an appropriate dictionary, one can easily check that they make no sense.

Suppose now that $G_1 = \{1\}$; then it follows from the cryptogram that $G_3 = \{3, 7, 8\}$, $G_4 = \{0, 4, 5, 6\}$. The correspondence between alphabetical characters and numbers now becomes

А	1	Ё	465	Л	783	С	4560	Ч	5460	Э	6450
Б	2 (29)	Ж	546	М	837	Т	4605	Ш	5604	Ю	6504
В	9 (92)	З	564	Н	873	У	4650	Щ	5640	Я	6540
Г	378	И	645	О	4056	Ф	5046	Ъ	6045		
Д	387	Й	654	П	4065	Х	5064	Ы	6054		
Е	456	К	738	Р	4506	Ц	5406	Ь	6405		

Answer. НАУКА (science).

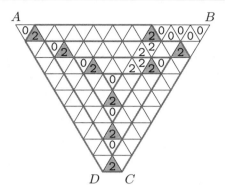

Figure 15

8.1   We divide the logo into equilateral triangles by drawing lines parallel to the edges of the logo (Figure 15). The gaps are marked with 0 and the overlaps with 2. For convenience, a few "empty" triangles are added at the top of the logo. Now there are as many 0-triangles as 2-triangles. The area of the band equals the area of the trapezoid $ABCD$. The numbers of triangles in the rows of $ABCD$ (from bottom) are $3, 5, \ldots, 19$. These nine numbers are seen to make up an arithmetic progression, hence their sum is

$$N = \frac{2 \cdot 3 + (9 - 1) \cdot 2}{2} \cdot 9 = 99.$$

Let h be the band width. The area of an equilateral triangle with height h is known to be

$$S_0 = h^2 \tan 30° = h^2/\sqrt{3}.$$

Denote by l the length of the band. The area of the band is $S = lh$. Therefore the desired relation is $l/h = 33\sqrt{3}$.

Answer. $33\sqrt{3}$.

8.2   Denote by 0^k (1^k) the sequence of k zeros (ones). The encrypting rules can be represented as

(1) $\begin{cases} 0 \to 0^{k_1} 1^{k_2} \\ 1 \to 0^{k_3} \end{cases}$ (rule I), $\begin{cases} 1 \to 1^{k_4} 0^{k_5} \\ 0 \to 0^{k_6} \end{cases}$ (rule II).

In a cryptogram, all the series of ones are of length either k_2 (rule I) or k_4 (rule II). For two cryptograms obtained from the same message to be identical it is necessary that

(2) $$k_2 = k_4.$$

It becomes now clear that in the message the number of zeros and ones should be equal.

Consider a message that consists of n zeros and n ones. Encrypting it by rule I, we get the cryptogram with $nk_1 + nk_3$ zeros while rule II gives $nk_5 + nk_6$ zeros. Thus

(3) $$nk_1 + nk_3 = nk_5 + nk_6.$$

It follows from (1) that the message must start with zero and end with one. Suppose that the first one in the message is preceded by a zeros. Upon encryption, the first $a + 1$ characters of the message are transformed as follows:

(4)
$$a = 1 \quad \begin{cases} 0^{k_1} 1^{k_2} 0^{k_3} & \text{(rule I)}, \\ 0^{k_6} 1^{k_4} 0^{k_5} & \text{(rule II)}, \end{cases}$$

$$a > 1 \quad \begin{cases} 0^{k_1} 1^{k_2} 0^{k_1} 1^{k_2} \ldots 0^{k_1} 1^{k_2} 0^{k_3} & \text{(rule I)}, \\ 0^{a k_6} 1^{k_4} 0^{k_5} & \text{(rule II)}. \end{cases}$$

For $a = 1$, we get $k_1 = k_6$, which together with (3) gives $k_3 = k_5$.

For $a > 1$ the following conditions must hold:

$$k_1 = a k_0, \ a > 0,$$

$$k_1 = k_5 + b k_0, \ b \geq 0.$$

Substituting the last expression for k_1 into (3), we get $k_3 = (1 - b)k_6$ and therefore $b = 0$. Consequently, $k_3 = k_6$, which together with (3) gives $k_1 = k_5$.

Finally, for $a > 1$ the necessary conditions take the form $k_2 = k_4$, $k_5 = k_1 = a k_6 = a k_3$, $a \in \mathbb{N}$. It follows from (4) that the message must be of the form $0 \ldots 0 1 \ldots 1$, where the number of zeros as well as the number of ones is a.

Answer. 1) For $k_2 = k_4$, $k_1 = k_6$, $k_3 = k_5$, any message of the form $0101 \ldots 01$ yields two identical ciphertexts.

2) For $k_2 = k_4$, $k_5 = k_1 = ak_6 = ak_3$, $a \in \mathbb{N}$, any message that looks like $(0 \ldots 01 \ldots 1) \ldots (0 \ldots 01 \ldots 1)$ (in each group there are exactly a ones and a zeros) provides identical ciphertexts.

Remark. Part 1) of the answer is not a special case of part 2) when $a = 1$.

8.3 Our enciphering sequence of 48 digits was originally built as a sequence of 24 primes $a_1, a_2, \ldots, a_{24}$. It is natural to assume that the people in question were born in the twentieth century. Hence $a_3 = 11$, $a_7 = 17$, $a_{11} = 47$, $a_{15} = 53$, $a_{19} = 83$, $a_{23} = 89$. The permissible neighbors of these primes are

prime	possible neighbors
11	13, 19, 43, 7, 3
17	13, 19
47	79, 43, 31
53	61, 37
83	79, 67, 19
89	97, 73

Another useful observation is that the first digit of a number specifying a month is either 1 or 0. The information we now have can be represented as

```
15 02 20 45 42 13 26 67 44 30 56 82 53 33 62 32 73 63 92 49 75 70 98 49
      19          19          19          19          19          19
      11          17       31 47       37 53 61    67 83       73 89 97
   03    03    13    13          43                      19
   07    07    19    19          79                      79
         13
         19
         43
```

Here the first line is our cryptogram, the second line contains the disclosed fragments of the message, the third line represents the known fragments of the key sequence; the other lines show permissible values of the corresponding primes.

Writing out the primes whose position is established, together with their possible neighbors, gives

11		17		31 47		37 53 61		67 83		73 89 97
03	03	13	13		43				19	
07	07	19	19		79				79	
	13									
	19									
	43									

Possible neighbors of 61 are 59 and 29 while the neighbors of 67 could be 59 and 3. Therefore, 59 is between 61 and 67. Possible neighbors of 73 are 89, 71 and 41. None of them can be a neighbor of 19 and only one of them, 71, can be a neighbor of 79. Thus the positions of 71 and 79 are established. Hence 47 goes after 43, and 41 must be between 43 and 37. With all the information accumulated, we have

11		17		31 47 43 41 37 53 61 59 67 83 79 71 73 89 97
03	03	13	13 29	
07	07	19	19 23	
	13			
	19			

The fragment 17 * * 31 is either (a) 17–19–23–31 or (b) 17–13–29–31.

In case (a)

11		13 17 19 23 31
03	03	
07	07	

Obviously 3 and 7 are the neighbors of 11. Therefore, 29 must be either next to 3 or next to 7, but none of the differences $29-3$, $29-7$ is a power of 2.

In case (b)

05	11		23 19 17 13 29 31
	03	03	
	07	07	

As in case (a), 3 and 7 are the neighbors of 11; 5 must appear before

3 because it cannot precede 19. Hence the number before 19 is 23, which, in turn, forces 7 to be after 11. Finally

15 02 20 45 42 13 26 67 44 30 56 82 53 33 62 32
10 09 19 48 29 04 19 54 25 09 19 49 12 06 19 71
05 03 11 07 23 19 17 13 29 31 47 43 41 37 53 61

73 63 92 49 75 70 98 49
24 06 19 70 04 07 19 52
59 67 83 79 71 73 89 97

Answer. 10.09.1948 29.04.1954 25.09.1949 12.06.1971 24.06.1970 04.07.1952.

8.4   Let the rows of the square be numbered $1, 2, \ldots, 13$ from top to bottom and the columns $1, \ldots, 13$ from left to right. Thus a pair of numbers $(i; j)$ is assigned to each cell; here i is the number of the row and j the number of the column.

The distance between the cells $(a; b)$ and $(c; d)$ is equal to $\sqrt{(a-c)^2 + (b-d)^2}$. Note that $|a - c| \in \{0, 1, \ldots, 12\}$ and $|b - d| \in \{0, 1, \ldots, 12\}$. Let $x = |a - c|$, $y = |b - d|$, $z = \sqrt{x^2 + y^2}$. Then $x^2 = (z + y)(z - y)$. Since z must be an integer, we have

$$1 = (z + y)(z - y) \Longleftrightarrow \begin{cases} z = 1 \\ y = 0; \end{cases}$$

$$2^2 = (z + y)(z - y) \Longleftrightarrow \begin{cases} z = 2 \\ y = 0; \end{cases}$$

$$3^2 = (z + y)(z - y) \Longleftrightarrow \begin{cases} z = 3 \\ y = 0 \end{cases} \text{ or } \begin{cases} z = 5 \\ y = 4; \end{cases} \text{ etc.}$$

$$12^2 = (z + y)(z - y) \Longleftrightarrow \begin{cases} z = 12 \\ y = 0 \end{cases} \text{ or } \begin{cases} z = 15 \\ y = 9 \end{cases} \text{ or } \begin{cases} z = 20 \\ y = 16 \end{cases} \text{ or }$$

$$\begin{cases} z = 37 \\ y = 35 \end{cases} \text{ or } \begin{cases} z = 13 \\ y = 5. \end{cases}$$

If $x^2 = mn$, then

$$z = \frac{m + n}{2}, \qquad y = \left| \frac{m - n}{2} \right|.$$

It is clear that 2 divides $m - n$. Taking into account that $y \leq 12$, the pairs $(x; y)$ for which z is a positive integer are

$$(x; y) \in A = \{(3; 4), (4; 3), (6; 8), (8; 6), (9; 12), (12; 9), (5; 12), (12; 5)\}$$
$$\cup \{(0; a), (a; 0), a = 1, \ldots, 12\}.$$

We say that a cell $(a; b)$ is *associated* with a cell $(c; d)$ whenever $(|a - c|; |b - d|) \in A$. The color of a cell changes only when Ciphy visits one of the cells associated with it. Since Ciphy touched each cell 1999 times, the color of a cell becomes finally reversed provided that this cell is associated with an odd number of cells.

Therefore our task is to determine for each cell the number of cells it is associated with, or more precisely, to find out whether this number is odd or even. By symmetry, it is enough to consider only those cells $(a; b)$ for which $a = 1, \ldots, 5$, $b = a + 1, \ldots, 6$. These 15 cells are numbered as shown in Figure 16. Any cell on a big diagonal of the square as well as any cell in row 7 or column 7 is associated with an even number of cells.

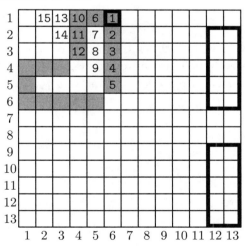

Figure 16

Consider the cell $(a; b)$. We say that a cell $(c; d)$ belongs to the *zone of asymmetry of the cell* $(a; b)$ if three cells symmetric to $(c; d)$

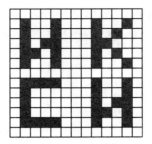

Figure 17

with respect to the row a, column b and the diagonal through the cells $(a; b)$ and $(a + 1; b - 1)$ lie outside the square. Obviously, for a given cell the number of associated cells lying outside its zone of asymmetry is even.

The zone of asymmetry for cell 1 is shown in Figure 16. All the cells of the 6×6 upper-left corner square that change their color are marked as gray.

Answer. See Figure 17.

8.6   Below we represent $2^{30} + 1$ as a sum of cubes, then as a sum of fifth powers and finally we write it by isolating a perfect square:

$$2^{30} + 1 = 2^{10 \times 3} + 1^3 = (2^{10} + 1)(2^{20} - 2^{10} + 1)$$
$$= 1025 \times (2^{20} - 2^{10} + 1) = 41 \times 25 \times (2^{20} - 2^{10} + 1),$$

$$2^{30} + 1 = 2^{6 \times 5} + 1^5 = (2^6 + 1)(2^{24} - 2^{18} + 2^{12} - 2^6 + 1)$$
$$= 65 \times (2^{24} - 2^{18} + 2^{12} - 2^6 + 1)$$
$$= 13 \times 5 \times (2^{24} - 2^{18} + 2^{12} - 2^6 + 1),$$

$$2^{30} + 1 = (2^{15} + 1)^2 - 2 \times 2^{15} = (2^{15} + 2^8 + 1)(2^{15} + 1 - 2^8)$$
$$= 33025 \times 32513 = 25 \times 1321 \times 32513.$$

This shows that 41, 13 and 5 divide $2^{30} + 1$. Straightforwardly, we get $32513 = 41 \times 793 = 41 \times 13 \times 61$.

It now remains to prove that 1321 is prime. To do this it is sufficient to check that no prime less than 37 divides 1321 ($37^2 = 1369$, $1369 > 1321$).

Answer. $2^{30} + 1 = 5 \times 5 \times 13 \times 41 \times 61 \times 1321.$

9.1 a) To prove statement a) it is enough to find one such sequence. As the desired sequence we can take the alphabet itself. Let us prove that the sequence that results does not have any letter repeated in it. For any two letters A_n and A_m ($m \neq n$) we must check that the numbers $2m$ and $2n$ give different remainders when divided by 33. It is clear that $m - n$ is not divisible by 33, hence 33 cannot divide $2(m - n)$. Thus statement a) is proved.

Remark. Statement a) remains valid for any alphabet with odd number of letters.

b) Denote by x the sum of the letters of the alphabet. Let y be the sum of the letters of the sequence resulted from addition of the alphabet and another sequence. For the letters of the resulting sequence to be all different, we must have $y = x$. At the same time, $2x$ and y must yield the same residue modulo 26. These two conditions hold simultaneously only if $x = y = 26k$, $k = 0, 1, 2, \ldots$. Computing straightforwardly $x = 1 + 2 + \cdots + 26 = 26 \cdot 13 + 13$, we see that x is not divisible by 26. This proves statement b).

Remark. Statement b) remains valid for any alphabet with even number of letters.

Another proof of b) offered by a participant of the Olympiad deserves consideration. For brevity, we will say that a letter A_n is odd (or even) if so is n. Adding two letters of the same parity, we get an even letter; adding two letters of opposite parity, we get an odd letter. Assume the converse, that is, there exists a sequence which upon addition with the alphabet yields a sequence of 26 pairwise distinct letters. This resulting sequence consists of 13 even letters and 13 odd letters. To obtain them we need 13 pairs of letters of the same parity and 13 pairs of opposite parity. However, 13 pairs of opposite parity contain 13 even letters and 13 odd letters, whereas in 13 pairs of the same parity the number of odd letters differs from the number of even letters because 13 is not divisible by 2. On the other hand, the sequences that we add up contain a total of 52 letters, 26 odd ones and 26 even ones. This contradiction proves statement b).

9.2 Here we write $a \equiv b$ if a and b yield the same remainder when divided by 33. Let n be the number of the first letter of the desired sequence. This letter was added 1949^{1949} times to К to give А. This can be written as

(1)
$$12 + 1949^{1949} \cdot n \equiv 1.$$

We have

$$1949^{1949} \equiv 2^{5 \cdot 399 + 4} \equiv (-1)^{399} \cdot 16 \equiv -16 \equiv 17.$$

Equation (1) takes the form $12 + 17 \cdot n \equiv 1$, or

(2)
$$17 \cdot n \equiv 22.$$

Now we multiply the number of each letter by 17 and reduce the products modulo 33. The result is shown next:

А	Б	В	Г	Д	Е	Ё	Ж	З	И	Й	К	Л	М	Н	О	П	Р
17	1	18	2	19	3	20	4	21	5	22	6	23	7	24	8	25	9

С	Т	У	Ф	Х	Ц	Ч	Ш	Щ	Ъ	Ы	Ь	Э	Ю	Я
26	10	27	11	28	12	29	13	30	14	31	15	32	16	0

It becomes clear now that equation (2) has a unique solution $n = 11$, hence the first letter of the sequence in question is Й. The other letters can be found similarly. The desired sequence reads

(3)   ЙЩНЧЛЖАФ

Adding this sequence 17 times to the word КРИПТОША, we get АНАЛИТИК. If we add this sequence 33 times to the word КРИП-ТОША, we get КРИПТОША again. Therefore, if we add the sequence (3) 16 times to the word АНАЛИТИК, the result must be КРИПТОША. The word КРИПТОША cannot be obtained in less than 16 additions. To prove this it is sufficient to consider the next-to-last letters of these words, Ш, И and А. It is clear that А must be added at least 16 times to И to give Ш.

9.3   Here we write $a \equiv b$ if a and b yield the same remainder when divided by 1000. To determine the last letter of the message, we must solve the equation

(1)
$$77 \cdot n \equiv 355.$$

Here n is a three-digit number to be found. Let $n = 100 \cdot a + 10 \cdot b + c$, where a, b, and c are decimal digits. Then

$$(100 \cdot a + 10 \cdot b + c) \cdot 77 \equiv 355$$
$$\Longleftrightarrow 7000 \cdot a + 700 \cdot b + 70 \cdot c + 700 \cdot a + 70 \cdot b + 7 \cdot c \equiv 355$$
$$\Longleftrightarrow 700 \cdot (a + b) + 70 \cdot (b + c) + 7 \cdot c \equiv 355.$$

This gives $c = 5$. Therefore

$$700 \cdot (a + b) + 70 \cdot b + 30 \equiv 0.$$

Hence $b = 1$. We have

$$700 \cdot a + 800 \equiv 0.$$

Thus $a = 6$, and therefore $n = 615$.

Equation (1) can be solved in a more elegant manner. Multiplying both sides of (1) by 13, we get $1001 \cdot n \equiv 13 \cdot 355$. The last three decimal digits of the product $1001 \cdot n$ coincide with those of n. Since $13 \cdot 355 = 4615$, we get $n = 615$. Solving (1) in which 355 is replaced successively with 850, 547, ..., we find the message to be

$$1213322526102218011501110 50615.$$

Answer. КЛЮЧШИФРАНАЙДЕН (The key of the cipher is found.)

10.1 The solution of the problem is illustrated in Figure 18. Scanning the relative positions of black strips in each row, we determine the color of some cells in rows 1, 2, and 15. These cells are marked with 1 enclosed in a circle if the cell is white, and with no circle otherwise. Then we scan the columns and mark with 2 the cells whose color has become evident. After that, we again scan the rows and mark cells with 3, and so on. The number in a cell is the number of the iteration at which its color was determined; white cells are marked with circled numbers.

Answer. See Figure 19.

10.2 Our task is to find all arrays (x, y, z, u, v, w) whose components satisfy the equation. There are 64 such arrays because each variable takes two values and $2^6 = 64$. We can merely try all of them. Roughly

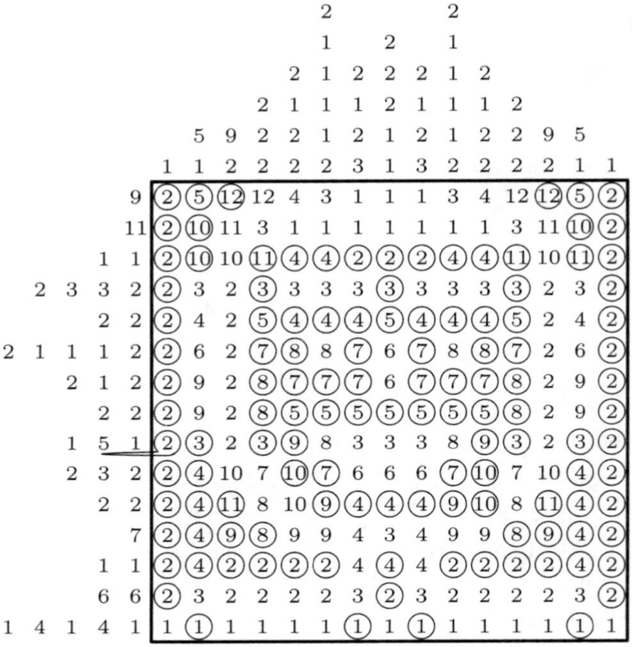

Figure 18

speaking, this requires 2^6 operations. However, the number of operations can be reduced to approximately $2 \cdot 2^3$. The trick is to compare all possible values of the left-hand side of the equation with those of the right-hand side. These values are

x	y	z	left-hand side		u	v	w	right-hand side
0	−1	1	−2		0	0	0	0
0	−1	2	2		0	0	1	3
0	2	1	−2		0	3	0	3
0	2	2	−1		0	3	1	3
1	−1	1	−2		−1	0	0	−1
1	−1	2	2		−1	0	1	1
1	2	1	1		−1	3	0	−1
1	2	2	2		−1	3	1	−2

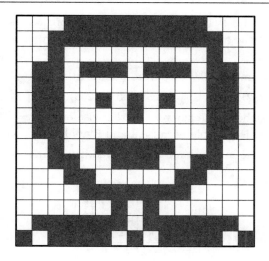

Figure 19

Upon inspection of the values obtained, we readily determine the desired arrays (x, y, z, u, v, w).

Answer. $(0, -1, 1, -1, 3, 1)$, $(0, 2, 1, -1, 3, 1)$, $(0, 2, 2, -1, 0, 0)$, $(0, 2, 2, -1, 3, 0)$, $(1, -1, 1, -1, 3, 1)$, $(1, 2, 1, -1, 0, 1)$.

10.3   A letter in column n of row m will be referred to as (m, n). It is clear that the encryption consists in replacing each letter (m, n) with the letter (n, m) or, what is the same, replacing each plaintext letter with that symmetric to it with respect to the main diagonal. Writing the ciphertext beneath the plaintext

H A N D W R I T I N G

H A V W D E M T M V P

we see that H, A, and T must be on the main diagonal. In addition, we get the following pairs of mutually symmetric letters: (N, V), (D, W), (R, E), (I, M), (P, G).

Now the analysis of the problem as a chain of trivial statements follows.

1. $T = (4, 4)$. If $T = (5, 5)$, then the keyword consists of the six last letters of the alphabet thus precluding the presence of H on the main diagonal.

2. By symmetry, $N = (1, 5)$ and $D = (2, 5)$.

3. $A = (2, 2)$. This is so because $D = (2, 5)$.

4. R must be in the keyword. Otherwise either $R = (4, 2)$ or $R = (4, 3)$. Neither is possible because R and E are located symmetrically.

With all the information accumulated, the square becomes

	1	2	3	4	5
1		IV	III	II	N
2	IV	A	B	C	D
3	III			I	
4	II		I	T	U
5	V	W	X	Y	Z

We have four available positions (shown by Roman numerals) for the three pairs (R,E), (I,M), and (P,G). The rest of the analysis is bulk and tedious but very simple, so we omit it.

Answer. SPRING.

10.4 Suppose T is a period of s_n; then $x_{n+T} - x_n$ must be divisible by 10 for each $n \in \mathbb{N}$. We have

$$x_{n+T} - x_n = \frac{(n+T)(n+T+1)}{2} - \frac{n(n+1)}{2}$$
$$= \frac{T(T+2n+1)}{2}.$$

It is clear that $T = 20$ is a period. Let us prove that any other period is not less than 20. For $n = 1$, we get

$$x_{1+T} - x_1 = \frac{T(T+3)}{2}.$$

The right-hand side is divisible by 10 for $T = 5, 12, 17$. However, for these values of T the difference

$$x_{2+T} - x_2 = \frac{T(T+5)}{2}$$

is not divisible by 10. Hence $T = 20$ is the smallest period.

Using the relation $x_n = x_{n-1} + n$, we find the numbers of the sequence $s_1, s_2, \ldots$ to be

$$1, 3, 6, 0, 5, 1, 8, 6, 5, 5, 6, 8, 1, 5, 0, 6, 3, 1, 0, 0, 1, 3, 6, 0, 5, \ldots.$$

The permutations p_k are as follows:

$$p_1 = (1360524789),$$
$$p_2 = (1865023479),$$
$$p_3 = (1506324789),$$
$$p_4 = (1023456789), \ p_5 = p_1, \ p_6 = p_2, \ldots.$$

The smallest period of the sequence $\{p_n\}$ is 4.

Answer. a) 20; b) 4.

10.5 The rule for rearrangement of letters is illustrated by the following example:

B	D	E	A	F	J	G	H	I	C
1	3	4	0	5	9	6	7	8	2
A	B	C	D	E	F	G	H	I	J

The first letter of the plaintext is placed above 0, the second letter of the plaintext takes the position above 1, etc. Using the permutations obtained in the solution of the previous problem, we get

```
L R H A G L I T S A|D A A C I T H E T N|T T D I I H S M E I
1 3 6 0 5 2 4 7 8 9|1 8 6 5 0 2 3 4 7 9|1 5 0 6 3 2 4 7 8 9
A L L R I G H T S A|I D T H E C A T A N|D T H I S T I M E I

V T A N I S H E D Q|I E O U L T S W L Y|E G I N B G I N N W
1 0 2 3 4 5 6 7 8 9|1 3 6 0 5 2 4 7 8 9|1 8 6 5 0 2 3 4 7 9
T V A N I S H E D Q|U I T E S L O W L Y|B E G I N N I N G W

T E I E T H H N D O|T F H E T A I L A N|E D G D N N I W I T
1 5 0 6 3 2 4 7 8 9|1 0 2 3 4 5 6 7 8 9|1 3 6 0 5 2 4 7 8 9
I T H T H E E N D O|F T H E T A I L A N|D E N D I N G W I T

T W I R H H E G N H|C M I A R H E I N E|S D O M E T I M E A
1 8 6 5 0 2 3 4 7 9|1 5 0 6 3 2 4 7 8 9|1 0 2 3 4 5 6 7 8 9
H T H E G R I N W H|I C H R E M A I N E|D S O M E T I M E A

T R E F H E T R E S|O G A H T F I T D O|E R N R C L A O L L
1 3 6 0 5 2 4 7 8 9|1 8 6 5 0 2 3 4 7 9|1 5 0 6 3 2 4 7 8 9
F T E R T H E R E S|T O F I T H A D G O|N E L C A R R O L L
```

Answer. "All right," said the cat; and this time it vanished quite slowly, beginning with the end of the tail, and ending with the grin, which remained some time after the rest of it had gone. *L. Carroll.*

11.1 Suppose the size of the text is l. Let x be the number of occurrences of a certain letter in this text. We can reformulate our problem as follows: find the smallest integer l for which there exists an integer x such that

$$\frac{10.5}{100} \le \frac{x}{l} \le \frac{11}{100}.$$

Some participants were guided by the erroneous assumption that the less x, the less l. However, for small x this is indeed so. For $x = 1$, l cannot be an integer. For $x = 2$, $l = 19$. Since $l \ge 100x/11$, we see that $l > 19$ when $x \ge 3$.

Answer. 19.

11.3 No matter how Ciphy rearranges the wires, the number of them in the representation of a letter remains the same. Let the wires be numbered in the order Ciphy arranged them, namely, the first wire corresponds to M, the second, to Q, etc. Suppose he connected the first wire correctly; then the received M could be D, F, G, J, K, M, the letters in the representation of which 1 appears exactly twice. Considering the other letters, we find their possible equivalents

number of ones	the first digit	possible letters
2	0	D F G J K M
1	1	Q
3	0	H L N O
1	0	H L N O
2	0	D F G J K M

No matter how we choose one letter from each row, we get an unintelligible word.

Suppose that the second wire should be at the first position. We have

number of ones	the first digit	possible letters
2	1	R S U Y
1	0	B C E I
3	1	T V W Z
1	0	B C E I
2	1	R S U Y

The first and the last letter of the original word must be the same, hence the word RIVER becomes evident at once.

The characters transmitted by the third wire coincide with those transmitted by the second wire, hence the case when the third wire is at the first position was already considered.

In the other cases (the fourth and fifth wire at the first position), we have

number of ones	the first digit	possible letters
2	0	D F G J K M
1	0	B C E I
3	1	T V W Z
1	1	Q
2	0	D F G J K M

number of ones	the first digit	possible letters
2	0	D F G J K M
1	0	B C E I
3	0	H L N O
1	0	B C E I
2	0	D F G J K M

These cases give us no intelligible words.

Answer. RIVER.

11.4 Suppose the cells are painted by colors $1, 2,$ and 3 as shown in Figure 20. Cells that form a line parallel to the main diagonal are painted by the same color. (The main diagonal goes from the upper-left corner to the lower-right corner.) Any three consecutive lines are painted by three different colors. Any three cells covered with a 1×3

1	2	3	1	2	3	1	2
3	1	2	3	1	2	3	1
2	3	1	2	3	1	2	3
1	2	3	1	2	3	1	2
3	1	2	3	1	2	3	1
2	3	1	2	3	1	2	3
1	2	3	1	2	3	1	2
3	1	2	3	1	2	3	1

Figure 20

tile are painted by colors $1, 2,$ and 3. Hence "good" cells (if they exist at all) are painted by color 1 because the number of the cells of color 1 is one more than that of the cells of color 2 and of the cells of color 3. Due to the symmetry, a $90°$ rotation of the table about its center takes each "good" cell to another "good" cell. The lines of color 1 before and after this rotation are shown in Figure 21(a). The cells having points of intersection as their centers are likely to be "good". As shown in Figure 21(b), they are "good" indeed. The keyword is

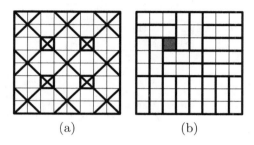

(a)   (b)

Figure 21

immediately found to be РУСЬ. To each letter of the keyword there corresponds a cipher alphabet:

А	Б	В	Г	Д	Е	Ё	Ж	З	И	Й	К	Л	М	Н	О	П
Р	С	Т	У	Ф	Х	Ц	Ч	Ш	Щ	Ъ	Ы	Ь	Э	Ю	Я	А
У	Ф	Х	Ц	Ч	Ш	Щ	Ъ	Ы	Ь	Э	Ю	Я	А	Б	В	Г
С	Т	У	Ф	Х	Ц	Ч	Ш	Щ	Ъ	Ы	Ь	Э	Ю	Я	А	Б
Ь	Э	Ю	Я	А	Б	В	Г	Д	Е	Ё	Ж	З	И	Й	К	Л

Р	С	Т	У	Ф	Х	Ц	Ч	Ш	Щ	Ъ	Ы	Ь	Э	Ю	Я
Б	В	Г	Д	Е	Ё	Ж	З	И	Й	К	Л	М	Н	О	П
Д	Е	Ё	Ж	З	И	Й	К	Л	М	Н	О	П	Р	С	Т
В	Г	Д	Е	Ё	Ж	З	И	Й	К	Л	М	Н	О	П	Р
М	Н	О	П	Р	С	Т	У	Ф	Х	Ц	Ч	Ш	Щ	Ъ	Ы

Decryption is as follows. For a ciphertext letter, we find the remainder after its number is divided by 4. Suppose the remainder is 1; we find the ciphertext letter in Р row, and the corresponding plaintext letter is in the same column of row А. If the remainder is 2, we should refer to У row, etc.

Upon decryption, the message is found to be as shown in Figure 22.

И	С	Т	И	Н	А	Н	Е
Р	О	Ж	Д	А	Е	Т	С
Я	И	╳	З	И	╳	С	Т
И	Н	Ы	Т	Ч	К	И	С
Т	И	Н	А	Р	О	Ж	Д
А	Е	╳	Т	С	╳	Я	И
З	О	Ш	И	Б	О	К	Т
Ч	К	К	А	П	И	Ц	А

Figure 22

Answer. a) "Good" cells are x-marked in Figure 22;

b) The keyword is РУСЬ.

The message is: Истина не рождается из истины. Истина рождается из ошибок. Капица[6]

---

[6]The truth is not borne by truth. The truth is borne by mistakes. Kapitsa (*P. L. Kapitsa*, Nobel Prize in physics, 1978).

Bibliography

[1] L. M. Adleman, C. Pomerance, and R. S. Rumely, *On distinguishing prime numbers from composite numbers*, Ann. Math., **117** (1983), 173–206.

[2] A. V. Aho, J. E. Hopcroft, and J. D. Ullman, *The design and analysis of computer algorithms*, Addison-Wesley, Reading, MA, 1974.

[3] W. R. Alford, A. Granville, and C. Pomerance, *There are infinitely many Carmichael numbers*, Ann. Math., **140** (1994), 703–722.

[4] D. Atkins, M. Graff, A. K. Lenstra, and P. C. Leyland, *The magic words are squeamish ossifrage*, ASIACRYPT-94, Lecture Notes Comput. Sci, vol. 917, Springer-Verlag, Berlin, 1995.

[5] M. I. Anokhin, N. P. Varnovskii, V. M. Sidel'nikov, and V. V. Yaschenko, *Cryptography in banking*, MIFI, Moscow, 1997. (Russian)

[6] A. Ashikhmin and J. Simonis, *Almost affine codes*, Des. Codes Cryptogr., **14** (1998), no. 2, 179–197.

[7] M. Bellare, S. Micali, and R. Ostrovsky, *Perfect zero-knowledge in constant rounds*, Proc. 22nd ACM Symp. on Theory of Computing, 1990, pp. 482–493.

[8] M. Ben-Or, *Probabilistic algorithms in finite fields*, Proc. 22nd IEEE Symp. Found. Comp. Sci., 1981, pp. 394–398.

[9] G. R. Blakley, *Safeguarding cryptographic keys*, Proc. AFIPS 1979 National Computer Conf., vol. 48, New York, 1979, pp. 313–317.

[10] G. R. Blakley and G. A. Kabatyanskii, *Generalized ideal secret sharing schemes and matroids*, Probl. Inform. Transm., **33** (1997), no. 3, 277–284.

[11] M. Blum, *Coin flipping by telephone: A protocol for solving impossible problems*, Proc. 24th IEEE Comp. Conf., 1993, pp. 133–137; reprinted in SIGACT News, **15** (1983), no. 1, 23–27.

[12] M. Blum and S. Micali, *How to generate cryptographically strong sequences of pseudo-random bits*, SIAM J. Comput., **13** (1984), no. 4, 850–864.

[13] S. Brands, *Untraceable off-line cash in wallets with observers*, Proc. Crypto'93, Lecture Notes Comput. Sci., vol. 773, Springer-Verlag, Berlin, 1994, pp. 302–318.

[14] E. F. Brickell and D. M. Davenport, *On the classification of Ideal Secret Sharing Schemes*, J. Cryptography, **4** (1991), 123–134.

[15] D. Chaum, *Online cash checks*, Proc. EUROCRYPT'89, Lecture Notes Comput. Sci., vol. 434, Springer-Verlag, Berlin, 1990, pp. 288–293.

[16] D. Chaum and T. P. Pedersen, *Transferred cash grows in size*, Proc. EUROCRYPT'92, Lecture Notes Comput. Sci., vol. 658, Springer-Verlag, Berlin, 1993, pp. 390–407.

[17] ———, *Wallet databases with observers*, Proc. Crypto'92, Lecture Notes Comput. Sci., vol. 740, Springer-Verlag, Berlin, 1993, pp. 89–105.

[18] H. Cohen, *A course in computational algebraic number theory*, Springer-Verlag, New York, 1993.

[19] H. Cohen and H. W. Lenstra, *Primality testing and Jacobi sums*, Math. of Comput., **42** (1984), 297–330.

[20] D. Coppersmith, A. M. Odlyzko, and R. Schroeppel, *Discrete logarithms in $GF(p)$*, Algorithmica, **1** (1990), 1–15.

[21] R. Cramer, R. Gennaro, and B. Schoenmakers, *A secure and optimally efficient multi-authority election scheme*, Proc. EUROCRYPT'97, Lecture Notes Comput. Sci., vol. 1233, Springer-Verlag, Berlin, 1997, pp. 103–118.

[22] R. Cramer, M. Franklin, B. Schoenmakers, and M. Yung, *Multi-authority secret ballot elections with linear work*, Proc. EUROCRYPT'96, Lecture Notes in Comput. Sci., vol. 1070, Springer-Verlag, Berlin, 1996, pp. 72–83.

[23] L. Csirmaz, *The size of a share must be large*, J. Cryptology, **10** (1997), no. 4, 223–232.

[24] D. Dolev, C. Dwork, O. Waarts, and M. Yung, *Perfectly secure message transmission*, Proc. 31st ACM Symp. on Found. of Comput. Sci., 1990, pp. 36–45.

[25] T. El Gamal, *A public key cryptosystem and a signature scheme based on discrete logarithms*, IEEE Trans. Inform. Theory, **IT-31** (1985), no. 4, 469–472.

[26] U. Feige, A. Fiat, and A. Shamir, *Zero-knowledge proofs of identity*, J. Cryptology, **1** (1988), no. 2, 77–94.

[27] P. Feldman, *A practical scheme for non-interactive verifiable secret sharing*, Proc. 28th ACM Symp. on Found. of Comput. Sci., 1987, pp. 427-437.

[28] A. Fiat and A. Shamir, *How to prove yourself: practical solutions to identification and signature problems*, Proc. Crypto'86, Lecture Notes Comput. Sci., vol. 263, Springer-Verlag, Berlin, 1987, pp. 186–194.

[29] M. Gardner, *A new kind of cipher that would take millions of years to break*, Scientific American, 1977, 120–124.

[30] M. R. Garey and D. S. Johnson, *Computers and intractability*, W. H. Freeman, San Francisco, CA, 1979.

[31] O. Goldreich and H. Krawczyk, *On the composition of zero-knowledge proof systems*, SIAM J. Comput., **25** (1996), no. 1, 169–192.

[32] S. Goldwasser and S. Micali, *Probabilistic encryption*, J. Computer System Sciences, **28** (1984), no. 2, 270–299.

[33] S. Goldwasser, S. Micali, and C. Rackoff, *The knowledge complexity of interactive proof systems*, SIAM J. Comput., **18** (1989), no. 1, 186–208.

[34] S. Goldwasser, S. Micali, and R. Rivest, *A secure digital signature scheme*, SIAM J. Comput., **17** (1998), no. 2, 281–308.

[35] O. Goldreich, S. Micali, and A. Wigderson, *Proofs that yield nothing but their validity for all languages in NP have zero-knowledge proof systems*, J. ACM, **38** (1991), no. 3, 691–729.

[36] D. M. Gordon, *Discrete logarithms in $GF(p)$, using the number field sieve*, SIAM J. Disc. Math., **6** (1993), no. 1, 124–138.

[37] J. Håstad, *Pseudo-random generators under uniform assumptions*, Proc. 22nd ACM Symp. on Theory of Computing, 1990, pp. 395–404.

[38] R. Impagliazzo and M. Luby, *One-way functions are essential for complexity based cryptography*, Proc. 30th Symp. on Found. of Comput. Sci., 1989, pp. 230–235.

[39] R. Impagliazzo, L. Levin, and M. Luby, *Pseudo-random generation from one-way functions*, Proc. 21st ACM Symp. on Theory of Computing, 1989, pp. 12–24.

[40] R. Impagliazzo and S. Rudich, *Limits on the provable consequences of one-way permutations*, Proc. 21st ACM Symp. on Theory of Computing, 1989, pp. 44–61.

[41] A. A. Karatsuba, *Basic analytic number theory*, Springer-Verlag, Berlin, New York, 1993.

[42] A. G. Kersten, *Shared Secret Schemes aus geometrischer sicht*, Mitteilungen mathem. Seminar Giessen, Heft 208 (1992).

[43] D. E. Knuth, *The art of computer programming*, vol. 2, *Seminumerical algorithms*, Addison-Wesley, Reading, MA, 1969.

[44] N. Koblitz, *A course in number theory and cryptography*, 2nd Ed., Springer-Verlag, New York, 1994.

[45] H. W. Lenstra, *Primality testing algorithms (after Adleman, Rumely and Williams)*, Lecture Notes Math., vol. 901, Springer-Verlag, Berlin, 1981, pp. 243–257.

[46] _____, *Elliptic curves and number-theoretic algorithms*, Proc. Intern. Congress Math. (Berkeley, CA, 1986), vol. 1, Amer. Math. Soc., Providence, RI, 1987, pp. 99–120.

[47] A. K. Lenstra and H. W. Lenstra, *The development of the number field sieve*, Lecture Notes Math., vol. 1554, Springer-Verlag, Berlin, 1993.

[48] A. K. Lenstra, H. W. Lenstra, M. S. Manasse, and J. M. Pollard, *The number field sieve*, Proc. 22nd ACM Symp. on Theory of Computing, 1990, pp. 564–572.

[49] F. J. Mac Williams and N. J. A. Sloane, *The theory of error correcting codes*, North Holland, Amsterdam, 1977.

[50] K. S. McCurley, *The discrete logarithm problem*, Proc. Symp. Appl. Math., vol. 42, Amer. Math. Soc, Providence, RI, 1990, pp. 49–74.

[51] M. Naor and M. Yang, *Universal one-way hash functions and their cryptographic applications*, Proc. 21st ACM Symp. on Theory of Computing, 1989, pp. 33–43.

[52] D. A. Plaisted, *Fast verification, testing, and generation of large primes*, Theor. Comp. Sci., **9** (1979), 1–16.

[53] K. Prachar, *Primzahlverteilung*, Springer-Verlag, Berlin, 1957.

[54] T. Rabin and M. Ben-Or, *Verifiable secret sharing and multiparty protocol with honest majority*, Proc. 21st ACM Symp. on Theory of Computing, 1989, pp. 73–85.

[55] H. Riesel, *Prime numbers and computer methods for factorization*, Birkhäuser, Boston, 1985.

[56] R. L. Rivest, A. Shamir, and L. Adleman, *A method for obtaining digital signatures and public key cryptosystems*, Commun. ACM, **21** (1978), no. 2, 120–126.

[57] J. Rompel, *One-way functions are necessary and sufficient for secure signatures*, Proc. 22nd ACM Symp. on Theory of Computing, 1990, pp. 387–394.

[58] C. P. Schnorr, *Efficient identification and signatures for smart cards*, Proc. Crypto'89, Lecture Notes Comput. Sci., vol. 435, Springer-Verlag, Berlin, 1990, pp. 239–252.

[59] P. O. Seymour, *On secret-sharing matroids*, J. Comb. Theory, Ser. B, **56** (1992), 69–73.

[60] A. Shamir, *How to share a secret*, Comm. ACM, **22** (1979), No. 1, 612–613.

[61] N. P. Varnovskii, *On the security of electronic signature schemes with hardware support*, Technical Report of the Moscow State Univ. Laboratory for mathematical problems of cryptography, 1997. (Russian)

[62] O. N. Vasilenko, *Modern primality testing*, Kibern. Sb., vyp. 23, 1986, pp. 51–99. (Russian)

[63] I. M. Vinogradov, *Elements of number theory*, 5th ed., Dover, New York, 1954.

[64] D. J. A. Welsh, *Matroid theory*, Academic Press, London, 1976.

[65] H. C. Williams, *Primality testing on a computer*, Ars. Combin., **5** (1978), 127–185.

[66] Y. Yacobi, *Efficient electronic money*, Proc. ASIACRYPT'94, Lecture Notes Comput. Sci., vol. 739, Springer-Verlag, Berlin, 1994, pp. 131–139.

[67] A. C. Yao, *Theory and applications of trapdoor functions*, Proc. 23rd Symp. on Found. of Comput. Sci., 1982, pp. 80–91.

Additional References

[68] R. Crandall and C. Pomerance, *Prime numbers. A computational perspective*, Springer-Verlag, New York, 2001.

[69] A. Kitaev, A. Shen, and M. Vyalyi, *Classical and quantum computations*, Amer. Math. Soc., Providence, RI, 2002.